A Gift to My Youngsters

By
Shaykh Mufti Saiful Islām

JKN Publications

First Published in June 2012

ISBN 978-0-9565504-9-1

British Library Cataloguing in Publication Data
A catalogue record for this book is available from the British Library.

Publisher's Note:

Every care and attention has been put into the production of this book. If however, you find any errors it is our own, for which we seek Allāh's ﷻ forgiveness
and reader's pardon.

Published by:

JKN Publications
118 Manningham Lane
Bradford
West Yorkshire
BD8 7JF
United Kingdom

t: +44 (0) 1274 308 456 | w: www.jkn.org.uk | e: info@jkn.org.uk

Book Title: A Gift to My Youngsters

Author: Shaykh Mufti Saiful Islām

Design & Layout by **iDesign** | e: IslamicDesign@jkn.org.uk

"In the Name of Allāh, the Most Beneficent,
the Most Merciful"

Contents

Introduction

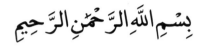

All Praises be to Allāh ﷻ. Peace and salutations be upon the last of the Messengers, our Beloved Prophet Muhammad ﷺ, upon his noble companions and upon those who follow their noble lifestyles until the final hour.

It is up to one individual to believe in a story, but the impact that it has on human life is far more than just words. This reminds me of a short story that had an impact on my life when I was a young person. I found it to be very enlightening and therefore wanted to share it with all of you.

Once Sayyidunā Eesā ﷺ was on a journey accompanied by his fellow companions. He gave some money to one of his companions and instructed him to get some food for everyone. The man took the money and went to a close by town. Since he was given rather a small amount of money, all he was able to buy were three loaves of bread. He was feeling very hungry and decided to eat one loaf of bread himself. When he rejoined the group, he handed the bread over to Sayyidunā Eesā ﷺ, who asked him, "Who ate the third loaf of bread?" The man nervously said that there were only two loaves of bread. Sayyidunā Eesā ﷺ did not say anything further and they resumed their journey.

Later on, the companions succeeded in hunting down a deer. They slaughtered the deer, cooked it, and were eating it when Eesā عليه السلام stood up and asked Allāh عز وجل to bring the deer back to life. In less than a second, the deer came back to life, jumped up, and ran away. All the companions were amazed that the deer that they just slaughtered, cooked and were eating from its flesh, all of a sudden came back to life. At this point Sayyidunā Eesā عليه السلام looked at the man who had gone to buy the bread and said, "I am asking you by the One Who brought this deer back to life, who ate the third loaf of bread?" The man retorted that there were only two loaves of bread. Sayyidunā Eesā عليه السلام again remained silent and the group continued on with their journey.

As they were walking, they came across a river that was over-flooded. Sayyidunā Eesā عليه السلام asked everyone to hold his hand. So everyone joined hands with him and thus they were able to walk on water across the over-flooded river. When they reached the other side, people marvelled at the miracle, "How could this be?! We just walked on water!" At that time Sayyidunā Eesā عليه السلام again turned to the man who had been sent to buy the bread and said, "I am asking you by the One Who made us able to cross the river by walking on water, who ate the third loaf of bread?" The man repeated, "There were only two loaves." Sayyidunā Eesā عليه السلام did not say anything further and they continued the journey.

Next they came to a desert where Sayyidunā Eesā عليه السلام took three big piles of sand and asked Allāh عز وجل to turn them into gold. As the man who had been asked to buy the bread was watching it, the piles of sand miraculously became piles of gold. Sayyidunā Eesā ﷺ then said, "One pile is for me, one pile is for you, the third pile is for the one who ate the third loaf of bread!" At this, the man instantly said, "I was the one who ate the third loaf of bread." Sayyidunā Eesā ﷺ then told him, "All three piles of gold are for you, but do not accompany us anymore."

The man did not care to have lost the company of Sayyidunā Eesā ﷺ and the other companions. He was so happy that he sat down in front of his new fortune and started to daydream about what he would do with all the gold. He was smiling all alone, looking at his wealth when suddenly three thieves came upon the scene. They saw this man sitting alone with a huge treasure of gold. The first thing they did was kill him. They then divided the gold. Each one of them took one of the piles of gold. Then one of the thieves was sent to get some food so they could eat and then plan out their future.

One of the thieves went to a nearby town to buy food. He decided to poison the food so that when he goes back, the other two thieves would eat the food and die, thus leaving him with all of the gold. So he poisoned the food and went back to rejoin the thieves.

His friends, who he left behind, were also plotting against him, thinking how to eliminate him in order to keep all the gold to themselves. So when he came back, they killed him and sat down to enjoy their meal. They ate the poisoned food and few minutes later they both died. When Sayyidunā Eesā ﷺ came back with his companions, they saw their former companion lying dead next to the three thieves and the three piles of gold. Sayyidunā Eesā عليه السلام pointed to the scene and said, "This is the life of this world and this is what it will do to those who seek after it."

Subhān-Allāh! We can see the outcome of this incident, how much of an impact and the moral lessons it contains. Similarly these interesting stories, events and moral lessons compiled in this book have great influence for those who take heed.

Allāh ﷻ reminds us in the Holy Qur'ān, **"Assuredly, in their narrative is a lesson for men of understanding. It is not a thing that has been forged, but a fulfilment of that which is before it and a detailed exposition of all things, and a guidance and a mercy to people who believe".**

Subscribers of our bi-monthly magazine 'Al-Mu'min', student and parents have requested my beloved Shaykh to compile a book that has wise sayings, interesting events and moral lessons from the Islāmic history for youngsters.

Taking the above suggestions into consideration, my beloved Shaykh has taken this task upon himself to compile this wonderful book *"A Gift to My Youngsters"*. This book is based on excerpts and passages collected from Al-Mu'min Magazine. These stories, wise sayings, admonitions and teachings have been compiled by my beloved Shaykh to give the readers especially our youngsters the opportunity of knowing what the great personalities of Islām have done with their lives, and how their purity of character has been an example for us to follow.

"A Gift to My Youngsters" has been put together to target primarily the younger generation of Muslims, but saying that, it will be of equal interest to all, whether they are youngsters or adults, and will help them develop good character and adopt intelligent behaviour in their lives.

Being extremely fortunate to be in the blessed service of my beloved Shaykh since the age of fifteen, I can proudly say that he is a man of noble character, a great orator, a deeply learned scholar of phenomenal intelligence, a prolific and versatile writer and a keen professor of Islamic Jurisprudence.

I pray that Allāh ﷻ accept his efforts and accept this valuable book and reward my beloved teacher and mentor for his sacrifices and efforts in propagating the religion of Islām. May Allāh ﷻ make the endeavour of my beloved Shaykh beneficial to myself and the entire Muslim Ummah. Āmeen.

Maulāna Ibrāhim Khān
Graduate, Jāmiah Khātamun Nabiyeen
April 2012/Jumādal Awwal 1433

The King and the Poor Man

There was a king who decided to take a tour of his country. As he passed by different places, everyone rushed to see him. However, while passing by a certain place, he noticed a poor old man who did not pay any attention to the king's arrival and remained engaged in his own activities. The king went up to this poor man and asked why he did not join the people to see him.

The poor man replied, "Before you, there was another king who passed this place. Everyone gathered to see him as well. But, a few days later he died and was buried in a place nearby. A poor man also died during that time and was buried near the king's grave. After some time, a strong flood passed through that area causing those graves to overturn. As a result, the bones of the poor man became mixed up with those of the king's. We could not differentiate between them any longer. After seeing this, it does not matter to me anymore as to who is a king and who is a beggar. In the end, our home is the same."

Mother

My love for you is something
that I never bother to explain,
O Mother, I'm ashamed for my behaviour
because all I gave you was pain.

You're the sweetest, tolerant
and most delicate of all,
O Mother, beneath your feet is Paradise
which I recall.

When I never spoke,
How could you always understand?
O Mother, you're a wondrous evidence
of Allāh's ﷻ tender guiding hand.

I remember just how important were
all those times together we shared,
O Mother, THANK YOU
It's what I wish I always said.

Even though I forget to show you my love,
So much more than I ever did,
O Mother, making an assumption you know it all,
is the error I made ever since I was a kid.

Now I am certainly assured
that without you I'd be lost,
O Mother, please forgive me once again,
because I can't ever lose you at any cost.

Holding on to My Faith

Holding on to my faith is like holding onto fire,
I want to let go and I want to retire.

I find it hard waking up for the Morning Prayer,
I can't take it no more, I just don't care.

Islām's too demanding, Islām's too much,
I want it all off my shoulders without making a fuss.
Do this and do that! Is all that I hear,
 I don't want to do anything, lets get that clear.

I'm a teenager for goodness sake,
Don't tell me when I die I'm going to get bitten by a snake.
I don't want to work hard; I want to chill with my mates,
I want to earn enough money to put food on my plate.
I don't want to hear the stories of the past,
I live in the present and I want that to last.

As long as I'm here I want a roof over my head,
I don't care what happens once I'm buried and dead.
Life is for living, let's get that straight,

Live it whilst you can before it's too late.
The end is a new beginning says my wise friend,
I just want to live in this world; I don't want it to end.

Well it is going to end! And it's not going to be nice!
And entry into Heaven isn't decided with the rolling of a dice.
Stop for a second and think why you're here?
Didn't God send any signs? Is it not clear?

Look in the Holy Qur'ān, it's all black and white,
Open your eyes, it's clear as daylight!
People all over are losing their lives,
And you're sitting at home eating your fries.

You take a sip of your milkshake and you think it's all cool,
Well it isn't cool when you're acting like a fool.
There's more to life than what meets the eye,
 And there's more to life after you die.

Time

Time has got me in it,
Looks like I'll have to get on with it,
There is no compromising with it,
It's not like I can deny it,
I am in existence through it,
Its not going to wait for me is it?
And there's not a single thing I can do to stop it,

I'm so busy; I'm totally blind to it,
Its definition is controversial,
but they all agree that you cannot live without it,
So I have the option to realize within it,
Or maybe I'll sit back and watch it,
And observe another in it,
Witness the lies, happiness,
laughs and tears through it,
Or I could just step back and let go of it,
Actually, I think I prefer taking advantage of it,
I swear there is something good at the end that is really worth it,
I don't have the might or power to stop it,
But I'm in control here of what I do with it,
Although it knowingly controls me and I fail to see it,
It's length is limitless it seems, or is it?

My mind cannot understand this to deal with it,
But there is a simple reason why its there and I know it,
Somewhere in there , my name is imprinted in it,
I just pray I don't get caught up and lost inside it.

Anyway back to reality...

What time is it ???

Sayyidunā Anas ﷺ
His Service to the Holy Prophet ﷺ

Today we will introduce you to one of the most beloved youngsters of Madeenah. His name was Anas ﷺ. His mother was Sayyidah Umme Sulaim ﷺ, a Mahram relative of the Holy Prophet ﷺ. Sayyidunā Anas ﷺ was still a small boy when his father, Mālik passed away. Sayyidah Umme Sulaim ﷺ thereafter married Sayyidunā Abū Talha ﷺ, who now became the step father of Sayyidunā Anas ﷺ.

Sayyidunā Anas Ibn Mālik ﷺ had great respect, intelligence and wisdom from a young age. He had great respect for his mother and served Sayyidunā Abū Talha ﷺ well.

During the early days after the Holy Prophet ﷺ had migrated from Makkah to Madeenah, Sayyidah Umme Sulaim ﷺ approached him and made a request, "O Messenger of Allāh ﷺ! Anas is an intelligent boy. You should keep him with you and he will be of great service."

The Holy Prophet ﷺ kept Sayyidunā Anas Ibn Mālik ﷺ with him. Sayyidunā Anas ﷺ then served the Holy Prophet ﷺ with all his heart and soul. He remained constantly with the Holy Prophet ﷺ and would aspire to serve the Holy Prophet ﷺ at every gesture. There were times when it was not even necessary for the Holy Prophet ﷺ to say anything and Sayyidunā Anas ﷺ through his

16

good judgement would run to carry out the desire of the Holy Prophet ﷺ.

The Holy Prophet ﷺ had a baby son, by the name of Ibrāheem. He was merely a few months old. He was born in a village close to Madeenah, at the home of a Sahābi called Sayyidunā Abū Saif ﷺ. Sayyidunā Abū Saif ﷺ was a blacksmith.

A blacksmith is a person who melts iron in a fire and shapes it into various items, like armoury, utensils, etc. Because of this trade the home of a blacksmith was always filled with smoke.

The Holy Prophet ﷺ would visit the home of Sayyidunā Abū Saif ﷺ in order to see his son, Ibrāheem. Sayyidunā Anas ﷺ would run ahead of the Holy Prophet ﷺ and forewarn Sayyidunā Abū Saif ﷺ to stall his activity so that the smoke does not cause inconvenience to the Holy Prophet ﷺ.

The Holy Prophet ﷺ would go there and pick his son up and play with him for a while before returning.

Once a woman (who used to sew clothes) invited the Holy Prophet ﷺ for a meal. She prepared a meal of pumpkin, meat and gravy. The Holy Prophet ﷺ accepted the invitation and Sayyidunā Anas ﷺ accompanied him. The Holy Prophet ﷺ loved to eat pumpkin and he sought out the pumpkin pieces in the gravy. When Sayyidunā Anas ﷺ saw this, he also acquired a taste and love for pumpkin, because it was beloved to the Holy Prophet ﷺ. This was the reason why Sayyidunā Anas ﷺ always had pumpkin cooked in his home.

The Holy Prophet ﷺ once sent him to fulfil a task. He affectionately and jokingly said that he will not go, but knew in his heart that he will fulfil the Holy Prophet's ﷺ wishes. He set off to complete the task but got delayed by becoming engaged in some play with other boys.

The Holy Prophet ﷺ was passing by when he saw Sayyidunā Anas ﷺ playing with the other boys. The Holy Prophet ﷺ affectionately got hold of Sayyidunā Anas's ﷺ nape. When he turned around he saw the beaming countenance of the Holy Prophet ﷺ, who whilst smiling asked him, "Anas, you have not completed the errand I sent you on?"

Sayyidunā Anas ﷺ replied, "O Rasūlullāh ﷺ! I am on my way!" after saying that, he ran off to complete the task.

Once the Holy Prophet ﷺ confided a secret to him and told him not to divulge it to anyone else. He revealed it to no one, not even his mother when he returned home.

The Holy Prophet ﷺ showered much Du'ā onto Sayyidunā Anas ﷺ, out of pleasure of his excellent service.

Sayyidunā Anas Ibn Mālik ﷺ had much Barakah (blessings) in his life and lived to a very ripe age.

Allāh ﷻ also blessed him with an abundance of wealth and sustenance. All this was the effect of the Du'ā of the Holy Prophet ﷺ.

A Pond Full of Milk

Once there was a king, who told some of his workers to dig a pond. Once the pond was dug, the king made an announcement to his people, saying that one person from each household, has to bring a glass of milk during the night and pour it into the pond. So, the pond should be full of milk by the morning. After receiving the order, everyone went home. One man prepared to take the milk during the night. He thought that since everyone will bring milk, he could just hide a glass of water and pour it inside the pond. Because it will be dark at night, no one will notice. So he quickly went and poured the water into the pond and came back. In the morning, the king came to visit the pond and to his surprise, the pond was only filled with water! What happened was that everyone was thinking like the other person that I don't have to bring the milk, someone else will.

My Beloved Youngsters!

When it comes to serve the Deen of Allāh ﷻ, do not think that others will take care of it. Rather, it starts from you, if you don't do it, no one else will. So change yourself to the way of Allāh ﷻ to serve Him, be obedient to Him, follow the Sunnah of the Holy Prophet ﷺ and that will make the difference.

The Smart Thing to Do

Here is a story of Sultān Mahmood of Afghanistan and his servant, Ayāz. Sultān Mahmood respected Ayāz for his wisdom even though he was a servant. This made the ministers and other people of high positions very jealous of Ayāz. They spoke ill of him and spread a rumour that Ayāz is nothing but a fool. The king came to know of this and he decided to prove to them who the real fools were.

An announcement was made to all people that the king will distribute his belongings on a particular date. Whatever a person touches will become his on that day. When the day came, many people appeared at the king's palace. The king made his announcement again that a person can have whatever he touches. The door opened and everyone rushed to touch whatever was valuable in the palace. Some touched jewellery of gold while others touched fancy furniture's etc. However, Ayāz stood by the king and did not touch anything. People thought that Ayāz was crazy because he was not taking advantage of this great opportunity. Now Ayāz asked the king if the announcement he made was certain. The king said, "Yes, whatever you touch is yours."

Immediately, Ayāz placed his right hand on the king's head and the left hand on his shoulder. He then shouted, "Listen everyone, I was waiting for this moment to acquire the most expensive thing. All of you took whatever the king possessed, but you forgot about the owner of all these, which is the king himself. I hereby declare that my hands are on the king, so the king is mine. You cannot remove anything from this palace because I am the owner of all these now." After hearing this from Ayāz everyone realised that actually, Ayāz is the only smart one and everyone else was in error.

My Beloved Youngsters!
Today people are only chasing the creation but very few are running towards the Creator Himself. If Allāh 🕮, the King of all kings, becomes our friend then who else do we need?

Do Not Expose the Faults of Others

Once when Al-Yazidi was gathered before their ruler Ar-Rashid, the time of Salāh set in, and they had to choose someone among them to lead the Salāh. It wasn't a difficult choice, because Al-Kasai was a well-known reciter of the Holy Qur'ān. Until this day, he is still known as one of the seven famous reciters. When the Salāh commenced and he completed the recitation of the opening chapter (Sūrah Al-Fātihah), he began to recite Sūrah Al-Kāfiroon.

Although this is among the shortest chapters of the Holy Qur'ān and memorised by many youngsters, Al-Kasai made a mistake in his recitation. After the completion of the Salāh, Al-Yazidi exclaimed with a surprise, "The reciter and the Imām of Kūfa being confused about, making a mistake, forgetting the chapter of Sūrah Al-Kāfiroon."

When the time of Ishā Salāh entered, Al-Yazidi did not wait (for Al -Kasai) but rather led the Ishā Salāh himself. As soon as he commenced the Salāh, his voice began to tremble and he forgot the opening chapter of the Holy Qur'ān, Sūrah Al-Fātihah.

When the Salāh was over, Al-Kasai said to Al-Yazidi, "Hold back your tongue and do not speak, otherwise you will be tested. Indeed, it is guaranteed for one to be put to trial when he opens his mouth."

Seven Wonders

A group of Geography students studied the Seven Wonders of the World. At the end of that session, the students were asked to list what they think were considered to be the present Seven Wonders of the World.

Though there were some disagreements, the following got the most votes:

1.   Egypt's Great Pyramid
2.   Taj Mahal
3.   Grand Canyon
4.   Panama Canal
5.   Empire State Building
6.   St. Peter's Basilica
7.   China's Great Wall

While gathering the votes, the teacher noted that one student, a quiet girl, hadn't turned in her paper yet. So she asked the girl if she was having trouble with her list.

The quiet girl replied, "Yes, a little. I couldn't quite make up my mind because there were so many."

The teacher said, "Well, tell us what you have, and maybe we can help."

The girl hesitated, then read, "I think the Seven Wonders of the World are:

1.   To touch
2.   To taste
3.   To see

She hesitated a little more, and then said:

4.   To hear
5.   To feel
6.   To laugh
7.   And to love."

Then there was the room, so full of silence it was deafening!

My Beloved Youngsters!
It is far too easy for us to look at the exploits of man and refer to them as 'Wonders' while we overlook all that the Almighty has done for us, regarding them as merely 'ordinary'.

May we be reminded today of those things which are truly wondrous that the GENEROUS CREATOR has given; that we take for granted!

"It is He Who has created for you (the faculties) of hearing, sight, feeling and understanding; little thanks you give." (23:78)

Story of a Truthful Young Boy

This is a story of a young boy who once departed on a journey for the pursuit of knowledge. His mother gave him forty Dinārs for expenses. She also made him promise that he would speak the truth under all circumstances.

A group of robbers intercepted the caravan. One of the robbers came to the young boy and asked him what he had. The boy replied, "Forty Dinārs."

The robber did not take him seriously and left him alone. Another of them put the same question to him and again got the reply, "Forty Dinārs." He got hold of him and took him to their leader who asked him the same question and then came the same reply, "Forty Dinārs."

The leader asked him, "Who has compelled you to speak the truth?"

The young boy repeated to him the promise he had given his mother. On hearing this, the leader was overwhelmed with awe. He tore off his clothes as if he was mad and said, "You don't violate the pledge that you have given to your mother. Here I am, unmindful of the word I have given to the Almighty, the Exalted, I violate it and I am not afraid in the least."

Then, ashamed and remorseful, he instructed his men to return all that they snatched from the caravan riders. Then he said, "I repent to the Almighty at your hands." Thereafter, all his associates repented and changed their lives. This young boy was none other than the honourable Shaykh Abdul Qādir Jilāni ﷺ!

My Beloved Youngsters!

"Truthfulness under any circumstances certainly has its merits, as illustrated by the above story. Lying is the worst of habits. It is our duty to keep away from the bad habits of lying and hypocrisy.

Islām declares, "Lying is a sign of the hypocrite." (Bukhāri)

"A liar invites the wrath and punishment of Allāh ﷻ." (Muslim)

Today's Lesson is...

The class sat in silence. Nobody dared to talk. Something was definitely wrong.

The teacher had just walked into the classroom and sat down with a very straight face. We would say our usual Salām to him, and he would reply, and that was about it.

Usually, the teacher would come in, sit down and say, "Today's lesson is…" But today he wasn't saying anything.

Everybody was looking down. Were we in trouble? Was the teacher angry with us? It was so quiet; we could hear the clock ticking in the background.

Suddenly, someone coughed. We looked up. It was Umar. He could never stay quiet for long! "Ummm…Ustādh what is today's lesson?" he asked rather sheepishly.

The rest of us were too scared to say anything. The teacher looked at him before looking at the whole class, then quietly he started…"Today's lesson is… SMILE!" and he gave us all such a big smile, that we couldn't help but smile back.

Relieved that we weren't in trouble, we looked at the teacher waiting for him to explain, "What a strange lesson we thought…" Still smiling, the teacher started his lesson…

"Right youngsters, you all know what Sadaqah is, don't you?

Sadaqah means charity and there is a lot of reward for giving charity. To give money to the poor is one way you can give charity, and Allāh ﷻ will reward you for it. But did you know, it's not all just about giving money?

Even if you were to move something harmful out of the path to save anybody from getting hurt, then that is also a type of Sadaqah.

But, did you know that just to smile at someone is also charity? And that you will be rewarded for it too?

What an easy way to get lots of reward! The Holy Prophet ﷺ was always smiling and would always try to keep everybody happy. Sayyidunā Husain ؓ, the grandson of the Holy Prophet ﷺ asked his father, Sayyidunā Ali ؓ about the Holy Prophet's ﷺ behaviour. Sayyidunā Ali ؓ replied, "He was always cheerful, gentle and mild."

In fact, the Holy Prophet ﷺ used to smile so much at everyone, that each one of the Companions thought that he was his favourite Companion! From this, we find that smiling is a Sunnah, and it is a very easy Sunnah which we all can follow, Inshā-Allāh.

Another good thing about smiling is that when you smile at someone, straight away they will smile back without even thinking about it, and you will help to make them feel happy.

So, next time you see anybody unhappy, give them a smile, because not only will you cheer them up, but you'll also be collecting reward at the same time. Even when you smile at your parents, our Prophet ﷺ has said that Allāh ﷻ will reward you with a reward equal to performing Hajj! Isn't that brilliant!!?

I'll tell you a little secret about myself kids, whenever I'm feeling unhappy or moody and fed up, I go and look at myself in the mirror and smile. This cheers me up straight away, as when we smile, our bodies release chemicals which make us feel good. Subhān-Allāh!!!

But please don't tell the other teachers as they'll think I'm silly for smiling at myself in the mirror! Anyway, next time when you are not feeling so good yourself, don't wait for somebody to smile at you, give it a try for yourselves. Smile and the world will smile back at you. You will feel better instantly."

I looked up at the other boys, everyone was listening so attentively. It had been a very interesting lesson. I left the classroom with one particular thought on my mind, I had to get that reward of a Hajj, it was so easy, how could I let that opportunity pass!? But before I got home, I bumped into Yūsuf, the new boy in the second year, he was very quiet and shy and quickly changed direction to avoid me. It was time to act upon the Sunnah..."As-Salāmu-alaikum Yūsuf!" I shouted and gave him a smile. He smiled back at me and replied, "Wa alaikumus-Salām." And as we walked home together, we had both made a new friend!

Do You Know How it Feels?

Do you know how it feels?
To be unsafe in your own home, to be tortured
just because of who you are.

Do you know how it feels?
To be frightened,
so much so that you're afraid of waking up
and living reality.

Do you know how it feels?
To have sleepless nights, because you're awake
constantly thinking about what horrors the
next day will bring.
Do you know how it feels?
To lose a loved one,
seeing them die right before your eyes
and to go through all that heartache and pain.

Do you know how it feels?
To live knowing that you're in danger,
to have nowhere to go because your home has been destroyed.

29

Do you know how it feels?
To be followed by armed tanks,
to be shot at with firing guns,
to be scared of the safety of your own life.

Do you know how it feels?
To watch innocent people die,
to watch their blood being shed,
to watch constant crying eyes filled with terror.

Do you know how it feels?

Do you know how it feels to be a Palestinian?

The Blind Boy

A blind boy sat on the steps of a building with a hat by his feet. He held up a sign which said, **"I am blind, please help."**

There were a few coins in his hat. A man was walking by. He took a few coins from his pocket and dropped them into the hat. He then took the sign, turned it around, and wrote some words. He put the sign back so that everyone who walked by would see the new words.

Soon the hat began to fill up. A lot more people were giving money to the blind boy. That afternoon the man who had changed the sign came to see how things were. The boy recognised the footsteps and asked, "Were you the one who changed my sign this morning? What did you write?" The man said, "I only wrote the truth. I said what you said but only in a different way." What he had written was, **"Today is a beautiful day and I cannot see it."**

The first sign and the second sign were saying the same thing. Of course both signs told people that the boy was blind. But the first sign simply told people to help by putting some money in the hat. The second sign told people that they were able to enjoy the beauty of the day, but the boy could not enjoy it because he was blind.

The first sign simply said the boy was blind. The second sign told the people they were so fortunate that they were not blind.

My Beloved Youngsters!

There are lessons we can learn from this simple story:

1.   Be thankful for what we have.
2.   Be creative. Be innovative.
3.   Think differently. There is always a better way.

Four Seasons of a Tree

There was a man who had four sons. He wanted his sons to learn not to judge things too quickly. So he sent them each on a quest, in turn, to go and look at a pear tree that was a great distance away.

The first son went in the winter, the second in the spring, the third in the summer, and the youngest son in the autumn.

When they had all gone and comeback, he called them together to describe what they had seen.

The first son said that the tree was ugly, bent and twisted.

The second son said no, it was covered with green buds and full of promise.

The third son disagreed, he said it was laden with blossoms that smelt so sweet and looked so beautiful, it was the most graceful thing he had ever seen.

The last son disagreed with all of them. He said it was ripe and drooping with fruits, full of life and fulfilment.

The man then explained to his sons that they were all right, because they had each seen ONLY one season in the tree's life. He told them that they cannot judge a tree, or a person, by only one season, and that the essence of who they are and the pleasure, joy and love that comes from life can only be measured at the end, when all the seasons are up.

My Beloved Youngsters!

If you give up when it's winter, you will miss the promise of your spring, the beauty of your summer, fulfilment of your autumn.

Don't let the pain of one season destroy the joy of the rest.

Don't judge life by one difficult season. Persevere through the difficult patches and the better times are sure to come.

Sneezing on a Boat

A pious person of former times, was once near the shore, where boats were leaving. A person sneezed on a boat and said, "Alhamdulillāh".

The pious person was on the shore when he heard this. In order to fulfill the reply of this sneeze, he hired a boat and approached the other boat. He only returned after replying to the person who sneezed. When all the people of the boat fell asleep, they suddenly heard a voice from the unseen proclaiming: "This person has purchased Jannah in return for one Dirham." (i.e. the fare of hiring the boat).

My Beloved Youngsters!

This pious person had travelled far and wide for the acquisition of knowledge and studied under more than 300 teachers and is non other than Imām Abū Dāwood ﷺ. His most famous Hadeeth book is Sunan Abū Dāwood.

Respecting the Name of Muhammad ﷺ

The king Nāsir-ud-Deen Mahmood had a servant called Muhammad who was with him most of the time.

Although the king always called him Muhammad, it so happened one day that the king called him Tāj-ud-Deen meaning the 'Crown of Deen'.

Although the servant did what the king told him at the time, he did not appear before the king for three days. When he finally came to the king again, the king asked him where he had been. He replied, "You always call me Muhammad so when you called me Tāj-ud-Deen, I thought that you were angry with me."

"Not at all," the king replied, "That was not the reason for not calling you by your name. I did not call you by your name that time because I did not have Wudhu and I feel that it is not appropriate to say the name Muhammad without Wudhu."

My Beloved Youngsters!

Subhān-Allāh! Look at how much respect the king had for the name of Muhammad even though he only called the servant. Whereas he never met the Holy Prophet ﷺ, the fact is that when someone loves another person, he loves everything attached to the person and respects it.

We must also bring Allāh's ﷻ greatness and love for the Holy Prophet ﷺ into our hearts, even when we see the name Muhammad written anywhere, we should show respect to it. We must say the Holy Prophet's ﷺ name with respect and never say or write his name without adding the words: "Sallallāhu alaihi wa sallam".

The Tolerance of Imām Abū Haneefah ﷺ

While Imām Abū Haneefah ﷺ was busy teaching, a man came up to him and started to swear at him. When his students wanted to respond to the man, Imām Abū Haneefah ﷺ stopped them. Neither did he allow them to respond, nor did he say anything himself. After the lesson was complete and he was going home, the foolish man followed him home and continued to swear at him.

When he reached the door of his house, Imām Abū Haneefah ﷺ turned to the man and said, "This is the door to my house, if you have anything left to say, please say it now so that nothing is left in your heart." The man was embarrassed when he heard this and could give no reply.

Because Imām Abū Haneefah 🌸 was an expert in the knowledge of Deen, he knew that it is not correct to reply to swearing by swearing back.

My Beloved Youngsters!

Neither did Imām Abū Haneefah 🌸 become upset by what the man was saying, nor did he say anything back to him. He practiced tolerance because had he said anything, he would have become more upset and the man would also have become more angrier and said many more hurtful things.

The wise behaviour of Imām Abū Haneefah 🌸 rather made the man embarrassed of himself. We should also do the same. If any person becomes angry with us for no reason, we should also remain silent and not make matters worse by arguing. The pious say, "Silence can defeat a hundred people."

The Intelligence of Sayyidunā Sulaymān عليه السلام

Sayyidunā Abū Hurairah ؓ reports from the Holy Prophet ﷺ that two ladies once came to Sayyidunā Dāwood عليه السلام. They had one child with them. Both of them claimed the child and that a wolf had eaten the other woman's child. Sayyidunā Dāwood عليه السلام decided that the child belonged to the elder of the two.

They left and were passing by Sayyidunā Sulaymān عليه السلام when he asked them what the matter was. When they explained the story to him, he asked someone to fetch a knife, saying that he was now going to cut the child in two and give a part to each of them. "Are you going to kill the child?" the younger lady asked. "Yes, I am," replied Sayyidunā Sulaymān عليه السلام. "Then you give the child to her," she said. Sayyidunā Sulaymān عليه السلام then said, "Then this must be your child." He then gave the child to her (younger lady).

My Beloved Youngsters!

The real mother did not want any harm to come to her child because her life, her time, her health and all her efforts are with the child. She was even prepared to suffer difficulty for the sake of her child.

This was exactly how the Holy Prophet ﷺ felt for his Ummah. May Allāh ﷻ grant us the same concern for the Ummah. Āmeen!

The Neighbour

Abū Hamza Sukri ﷺ was a famous narrator of Ahādeeth. "Sukkur" means sweetness in Arabic and it is written that he was given this title because his manner of speaking was very pleasant and very sweet. Whoever heard his talks was captivated by him

He lived in a certain part of Baghdad. One day, he decided to leave the area and move somewhere else and had almost sold his house when the people heard about this. They got together and sent some men to plead to him not to move. They begged him to stay, but he explained to them his reasons. They then decided that they would put their money together and pay him the price for his house so that he could stay and remain their neighbour. When he saw that they were sincere, he cancelled his plans to move.

My Beloved Youngsters!

Subhān-Allāh! Look at how some people are so well liked because of their excellent character and because they do good only to please Allāh ﷻ and not to please the people.

The Holy Prophet ﷺ said that Sayyidunā Jibreel ﷺ told him so much about the rights of the neighbours that he thought that the neighbour would even receive a share of inheritance.

The Baker's Loss

A baker put a selection of delicious pastries on a tray. He carried the tray to the street market and offered pastries for sale. A joker looked at all the wonderful treats. He asked the baker, "How much do you want for all the pastries on the tray?" The baker replied that he hoped to make ten pounds.

The joker offered an odd deal. He said, "I will give you ten pounds if you will eat all the pastries yourself. I will stand here and watch you eat all of them, and then I will give you the ten pounds."

The baker agreed. He began eating all the little cakes and cookies. The joker watched as the baker ate until the last pastry was gone. Then the joker laughed and ran away without giving the baker any money.

The baker could not even call the police and claim to be a victim. He had eaten his own baked items. He had caused his own loss. The police would not make the joker pay for the pastries when he was not the one who had eaten them all.

My Beloved Youngsters!

Shaytān the evil whisperer is like the joker. He tries to trick us by offering to reward us for robbing our own souls. In the end, however, we are left to pay for our own bills.

The Holy Qur'ān teaches us, **"Whosoever accepts guidance does so for their own benefit. Whosoever rejects guidance does it for their own loss. No sinner is responsible for another's sins. We do not punish without first sending a messenger."** (17:15)

Allāh ﷻ says in the Holy Qur'ān, **"Whosoever brings a good deed, he shall be rewarded ten like it and whosoever brings an evil deed he shall be recompensed only with the like and they shall not be dealt with unjustly."** (6:160)

Do not let the evil whisperer trick you. He is a mean joker. If you do something wrong he will laugh at you. He will not pay for your loss.

A Person's True Friend

It is reported that a man had three friends. Although he liked the first two more, it was actually the third one who was an excellent and sincere person.

One day, he was accused of doing something he did not do and was called to appear in court. He therefore called for his friends and said, "You all know that I am innocent and that I will be found guilty if at least one of you does not prove to the judge that I am innocent."

The first friend whom he loved most excused himself saying, "I cannot stand with you because I have many other relatives to worry about."

The second one went with him to the court, but when he reached the doors, he grew scared and turned back. It was the third friend that went inside with him.

When they went in, the friend spoke to defend the man and the judge accepted what he had to say. The man was then set free.

The three friends in this story are actually a person's wealth, family and good deeds. While a person loves his wealth the most and thinks it will be most beneficial to him, it will not come with him to the grave.

His family and friends will only take him to the grave, but will then turn back and leave him all alone.

It will only be his good deeds that will then go with him in the grave and will also stand with him on the Day of Judgement, where it will speak up for him and have Allāh's ﷻ mercy showered upon him.

My Beloved Youngsters!

Our real friend is the one whom we pay the least attention to. An intelligent person will rather spend more time and effort on that which is of benefit to him. He will make sure that he does good deeds, stays away from sins and fulfils all the rights he owes to Allāh ﷻ and to other people. He must also thank Allāh ﷻ for giving him the ability to do all this.

Beloved Youngsters! You should know that when a person enters the grave, his good deeds surround his body and appear in a beautiful and fragrant smelling form to keep him company. From today, we must make the intention to do many good deeds and to tell others to do the same, so that we can all be successful in this world and in the Ākhirah.

Generosity

Sayyidunā Abdullāh Ibn Mubārak ﷺ had plenty of wealth in this world, but his heart remained free of any love for it. He was blessed with the special quality that saints speak about when they say, "Wealth should remain in the hand and never enter the heart." When he was living in Khurāsān, he decided to go for Hajj. The people of the town sent a group of people with the request, "We have heard that you intend going for Hajj, so if you permit, we would like to join you to benefit from your company."

"That will be fine," Sayyidunā Abdullāh ﷺ replied, "But I would want you all to leave your monies with me so that I may spend for us all." The people readily agreed and he took all their bags of money and placed it in a box. He then saw to all the expenses of the journey as they travelled.

After completing Hajj, when they reached Madeenah, he asked them what their families at home had asked them to buy from Madeenah.

They told him what it was and he took them all to the marketplace to buy whatever they wanted. Thereafter, he took them back to Makkah and again asked them what their families had asked them to buy from there. They told him what it was and he took them all to the marketplace to buy whatever they wanted.

After this they returned home to Khurāsān, where he invited them all for a meal. After the meal, he gave them all gifts and then opened up the box and gave each one of them their bags of money back.

My Beloved Youngsters!

This story teaches us that every person should spend the wealth Allāh ﷻ gives him in doing good according to his means. In this way, Allāh ﷻ will give him blessings in his wealth. He must of course, make sure he does not spend the money in the wrong places.

The Wise Grandsons

Once the grandsons of the Holy Prophet ﷺ, Sayyidunā Hasan ؓ and Sayyidunā Husain ؓ saw an old man performing Wudhu at the banks of the Euphrates river. The man hastened through the Wudhu and performed Salāh just as quickly. In doing so, he omitted the Sunnah method of Wudhu and Salāh.

Sayyidunā Husain ؓ wanted to teach the old man the correct method, but they feared that he being old, would be insulted if his error was pointed out by them.

They approached him and said, "We are young and you are an old man with lots of experience. You know how to perform Wudhu and Salāh better than us. We would like to perform Wudhu and Salāh in your presence and we would appreciate it, if you would point out to us any errors we might commit."

Thereafter, they proceeded to perform Wudhu and Salāh according to the Sunnah method. When the old man saw this, he immediately repented from his wrong and rectified himself.

That is a Crow, My Son

A man had become very old. He had given his son the best of education and given all he could. One day he was sitting outside with his son when a crow perched on the wall. "Son, what is that?" the father asked. "That is a crow, father," the son replied.

After a short while, the father again asked, "Son! What is that?" "That is a crow, father," the son repeated. It was not long afterwards that the father again asked, "Son! What is that?" The son said, "I just told you, that is a crow, father!"

They sat still and quiet for a while and again the father asked, "Son! What is that?" The son's tone changed this time as he said,

44

"That is a crow, father! A crow!"

Yet again, the father asked the son, "Son! What is that?" This time the son could not contain himself. "That is a crow, father!!" he shouted, "You keep asking the same question all the time, I have told you a thousand times that is a crow. Don't you understand me!?"

A little while later, the father got up, went to his room and took out an old diary. He opened up one of the pages and handed the diary over to his son saying, "Son, please read this."

The son read: Today my little boy was sitting in the yard when a crow arrived. He then asked me twenty five times, "Daddy! What is that?" I then replied each one of the twenty-five times, "Son, that is a crow." Each time I replied with great love and affection.

The father then said, "Son, see the difference between a father and son. While I replied twenty-five times and even noted that it was with love and affection each time. Today you got angry when I asked you the same question five times."

My Beloved Youngsters!

We forget the good that our parents did for us. We do not know how many times they have gone out of their way to do things for us. We must make a pledge that we will never speak to them disrespectfully and that we will speak to them in a soft and affectionate voice. We must never have pride because Allāh ﷻ does not like it at all and will punish a person for it.

Making Time to Acquire Knowledge

There were several islands in a certain area but not all of them had schools. The youngsters therefore needed to travel by ferry to attend school.

One day, the youngsters got up to mischief and decided to make fun of the ferryman. One child therefore went up to the ferryman and said, "Sir! Do you know mathematics?" When the ferryman replied that he knew none of it, the child remarked, "You have wasted half your life." All the youngsters then started to laugh.

A little while later, another child went up to the ferryman and said, "Sir! Do you know history?" When the ferryman replied that he knew none of it, the child remarked, "You have wasted half your life." All the youngsters again started to laugh.

A little while later, another child went up to the ferryman and said, "Sir! Do you know science?" When the ferryman again replied that he did not know, the child remarked, "You have wasted half your life." Yet again, all the youngsters started to laugh.

In this manner, they continued making fun of the man. Meanwhile, a storm brewed and it began to rain. The waves shook the ferry about and it was on the verge of sinking.

Now it was the ferryman's turn. "O youngsters!" he called out, "Do you know how to swim!?" "No!" they replied, "We do not know!" He then said to them, "You have then wasted your lives."

My Beloved Youngsters!

This will be the case on the Day of Judgement. Whereas people today are telling the scholars that they have wasted half their lives, on the Day of Judgement, they will realise that it was them who wasted their lives. Think about what will happen there. There is a very small percentage of people who have been entrusted to safeguard the interest of the Deen (i.e. the scholars).

They have studied every verse of the Holy Qur'ān together with its proper meaning and are always defending the Deen from the floods of trouble that attack it from every side. This they are doing because it is the command of Allāh ﷻ. Now, instead of the people who are unaware of the Deen dragging the small percentage of scholars into the field of science, they should call them and rather learn the Deen from them.

Lesson! Through this incident our elders wish to teach us that instead of having regrets on the Day of Judgement, we must learn about our Deen now and practice on this knowledge.

47

Another lesson they wish to teach us is that Allāh ﷻ has made the system of the world such that He has given different roles to different people.

Just as we cannot tell all doctors to start planting vegetable fields, it will also be foolish for us to shift the limited amount of scholars from the task of spreading and teaching the Deen and to engage them in other jobs and in acquiring other types of knowledge.

A Glass Of Milk

One day a poor boy was selling goods door to door, to pay his way through school. He discovered he only had one pound and he was hungry.

He decided he would ask for a meal at the next house. However, he lost his nerve when a young woman opened the door. Instead of asking for a meal he asked for a drink of water.

The young lady thought he looked hungry; so she brought him a large glass of milk. He drank it slowly and asked, "How much do I owe you?" "You don't owe me anything," she replied, "Mother has always taught us never accept payment for kindness." The boy said, "Then I thank you from the bottom of my heart."

As the little boy left that house, he not only felt stronger physically, but his faith in Allāh ﷻ became stronger. He had been ready to give up and quit, but continued.

Years later that young woman became critically ill. The local doctors were baffled. They sent her to the hospital, where they called a specialist to study her rare disease. Dr. Abdullāh was called in for the consultation.

When he heard the name of the town she came from, a strange light filled his eyes. Immediately he rose and went down the hall of the hospital to her room.

Dressed in his doctor's gown he went in to see her. He recognised her at once. He went back to the consultation determined to do his best to save her life within his capacity. From that day he gave special attention to the cause.

After a long struggle, the battle was won. Dr. Abdullāh requested the nurse to pass the final bill to him for approval.

He looked at it, then wrote something on the edge of the bill and sent it to her room. She feared to open it, for she was sure it would take the rest of her life to pay for it.

Finally she looked and something caught her attention on the side of the bill.

She read these words: Paid in full with one glass of milk, signed Dr. Abdullāh.

Kindness Towards the Creation

Bāyazeed Bustāmi ﷺ was a famous saint who lived a long time ago. His story is a very famous one. After he had passed away, someone saw him in a dream and asked, "How did Allāh ﷻ treat you?" He replied, "Something very strange happened to me. When I reached Allāh ﷻ, He asked me what action I had brought. I thought for a while about what reply to give. What action could I present? Because I could find nothing to present to Allāh ﷻ I said, "O Allāh! I have brought nothing. I have come with empty hands and have nothing to hope for besides Your mercy and generosity."

Allāh ﷻ then said to me, "While you had carried out many good deeds there was one particular deed that I loved very much. It is because of that single deed that I shall forgive you today. The deed was carried on that night when you woke up and found a kitten shivering in the cold. Taking pity on the poor creature, you made a place under your blanket and kept him there. In the warmth of your blanket, the kitten spent the entire night in peace and safety from the cold. That night, the kitten prayed to Me saying, "O Allāh! Just as this man has given me safety from the cold, You give him safety from the heat of the Day of Judgement." Since you did this solely for My pleasure and for no other reason, I loved this action very much and I shall forgive all your sins because of it."

Bāyazeed Bustāmi ﷺ says, "Although I have achieved plenty of knowledge and recognition of Allāh ﷻ in this world, the one cause for my safety was kindness to Allāh's ﷻ creation."

We can imagine that if a person is rewarded so much for treating an animal kindly, how much more would he be rewarded for treating the best of creation kindly.

Furthermore, amongst the best of creation, how much more will he be rewarded for treating a Muslim kindly?

Even more than this, the rewards are even greater for treating one's brothers, sisters, relatives and parents kindly.

We will be very foolish if we let the opportunity pass us and we do not treat relatives and strangers with kindness. In fact, we should be a means of peace and comfort to all people and should not cause them any harm. The most important thing about good character is that no person should be harmed by our actions.

My Beloved Youngsters!

From today make a firm intention never to cause any harm to your parents, brothers, sisters, relatives, friends, neighbours, animals, plants and all creations of Allāh ﷻ.

Love for the Holy Prophet ﷺ

When the treaty of Hudhaibiyah was taking place, the Quraysh of Makkah sent Urwa Ibn Mas'ood Thaqafi to speak for them. Urwa was a very intelligent and observant person.

As soon as he came to the Muslim camp, he looked at everything very carefully and even while talking to the Holy Prophet ﷺ he took notice of how the Sahābah ؓ behaved. When he went back to the Quraysh in Makkah, he had the following to say about how the Sahābah ؓ would give their lives for the Holy Prophet ﷺ.

He said, "O my people! I have been sent to the kings of Rome, Persia and Ethiopia. However, I swear by Allāh ﷻ that I have never seen the companions of any king show as much respect to their king as I have seen the Companions of Muhammad ﷺ show to him. I swear by Allāh ﷻ that even when he spits, one of them puts out his hand to grab it. When he performs Wudhu, they compete with each other to get the water falling off his body and when he gives a command, they run to carry it out. When he speaks, they all become silent and they always look at him with great love and affection."

It is difficult to use better words than these to explain the respect that the Sahābah ؓ showed to the Holy Prophet ﷺ.

When a person is praised by his enemy, the words carry much more weight. Blessed were those Companions who managed to soften the hard hearts of their enemies by their excellent behaviour and manners.

Once a pious saint said, "Respect is a crown that is received by Allāh's ﷻ kindness and mercy. Allāh ﷻ places it on the head of whoever He wills."

Sayyidunā Anas Ibn Mālik ؓ says that whenever the Sahābah ؓ needed to see the Holy Prophet ﷺ for something important, they would knock with their nails rather than their knuckles. In this way, they would not be disturbing him with too much noise and he would still be able to hear them.

My Beloved Youngsters!

We must also show great respect to our elders, our parents, teachers and pious people. We must be quiet in front of them and never misbehave when they are around. We must listen to all they say and never do anything disrespectful.

When returning home, we should not bang at the door, but knock lightly and then close the door gently when coming in. We must listen silently when our parents tell us something and never backbite when they discipline us.

An Encounter with a Thief

Sayyidunā Abū Hurairah ؓ narrates the following Hadeeth: The Holy Prophet ﷺ deputed me to safeguard the Sadaqatul-Fitr of Ramadhān. Someone came and started taking handfuls of the foodstuff (of the Sadaqah) secretly. I took hold of him and said, "By Allāh ﷻ, I will take you to the Holy Prophet ﷺ." He said, "I am needy and have many dependants, and I am in great need." I let him go.

In the morning the Holy Prophet ﷺ asked me, "What did your prisoner do yesterday?" I said, "O Rasūlullāh ﷺ, the person complained of being needy and having many dependants, so I pitied him and let him go."

The Holy Prophet ﷺ said, "Indeed he told you a lie and he will be coming again soon."

I believed that he would show up again as the Holy Prophet ﷺ had told me that he would return. So, I waited for him watchfully. When he showed up and started stealing handfuls of foodstuff, I caught hold of him again and said, "I will definitely take you to the Holy Prophet ﷺ. He said, "Leave me alone for I am needy and have many dependants. I promise I will not come back again." I pitied him and let him go.

In the morning the Holy Prophet ﷺ asked me, "What did your prisoner do yesterday?" I said, "O Rasūlullāh ﷺ, the person complained of being needy and having many dependants, so I pitied him and let him go."

The Holy Prophet ﷺ said, "Indeed he told you a lie and he will be coming again soon."

I waited for him attentively for the third time, and when he came and started stealing handfuls of the foodstuff, I caught hold of him and said, "I will surely take you to the Holy Prophet ﷺ and it is your third time, you promised not to return, yet you come back and break your promise." He said, "Forgive me and I will teach you some words with which Allāh ﷻ will benefit you." I asked, "What are they?" He replied, "Whenever you go to bed, recite Āyatul Kursi - Allāhu lā ilāha illā huwal Hayyul Qayyūm (Allāh, there is none worthy of worship except You, the Ever-Living the One Who sustains and protects all that exists) [Sūrah Al-Baqarah verse 255] till you finish the whole verse. If you do so, Allāh ﷻ will appoint a guard for you who will stay with you and no Shaytān will come near you till morning." So I released him.

In the morning the Holy Prophet ﷺ asked me, "What did your prisoner do yesterday?" I replied, "He claimed that he would teach me words by which Allāh ﷻ will benefit me, so I let him go."

The Holy Prophet ﷺ asked, "What were they?" I replied, "He said to me, whenever I go to bed recite Āyatul Kursi from the beginning to the end. He further said to me, if you do so Allāh ﷻ will appoint a guard for me who will stay with me, and no Shaytān will come until morning."

The Holy Prophet ﷺ said, "He really did speak the truth, although he is an absolute liar. Do you know who you was talking to all these three nights O Abū Hurairah?" I replied, "No." Then the Holy Prophet ﷺ said, "Indeed it was Shaytān." (Bukhāri)

When You Thought I wasn't Looking

To my Beloved Parents,

When you thought I wasn't looking, I saw you hang my first painting on the refrigerator, and I immediately wanted to paint another one.

When you thought I wasn't looking, I saw you feed a stray cat, and I learnt that it was good to be kind to animals.

When you thought I wasn't looking, I saw you make my favourite cake for me, and I learnt little things can be the special things in life.

When you thought I wasn't looking, I heard you make Du'ā, and I knew that there is always Allāh ﷻ I can talk to, and I learnt to trust in Him.

When you thought I wasn't looking, I saw you make a meal and take it to a friend who was sick, and I learnt we all have to help take care of each other.

When you thought I wasn't looking, I saw you give your money and time to help people who had nothing and I learnt that those who have something should give to those who don't.

When you thought I wasn't looking, I saw you take care of your household and everyone in it, and I learnt that we have to take care of what we are given.

When you thought I wasn't looking, I saw how you handled your responsibilities, even when you didn't feel good, and I learnt that I have to be responsible when I grow up.

When you thought I wasn't looking, I saw tears come from your eyes, and I learnt sometimes things hurt, but it's alright to cry.

When you thought I wasn't looking, I saw that you cared and that I wanted to be everything I could be.

When you thought I wasn't looking, I learnt most of life's lessons that I need to know to be a good and productive person when I grow up.

When you thought I wasn't looking, I wanted to look at you and say, "Thanks for all the things I saw when you thought I wasn't looking."

The Imān of the Little Boy

There was a king who lived a long time ago. When his magician became old, he approached the king and requested him to send someone to him so that he could teach him magic. The king wanted someone to continue the practice after the old magician, so he sent a boy to take lessons from the magician.

Whenever the boy came to the magician, he had to pass by a Christian monk, who believed in Sayyidunā Eesā ﷺ. During those days, the Deen of Sayyidunā Eesā ﷺ was the true Deen and the monk was pious and stayed far from the evils of the people.

It once occurred that a lion blocked the path and prevented people from passing. When the boy arrived there, he thought to himself that this would be the ideal opportunity to test whether the magician or the monk was better. He therefore picked up a stone and prayed, "O Allāh ﷻ! If the way of the monk is more beloved to You than the way of the magician, then kill this beast with this stone so that people may pass."

Consequently, when he threw the stone at the creature, the stone killed it instantly and people were able to pass by peacefully. The people were surprised and the boy became famous. When a blind man heard about the boy, he went to him and asked him to cure him of his blindness. The boy said, "I cannot cure anyone. Only Allāh ﷻ can cure. However, if you believe in Allāh ﷻ, I will pray to Allāh ﷻ and He will cure you." When the man became a Muslim, Allāh ﷻ restored his sight.

When the king heard about this, he arrested the monk, the blind man and the boy. He then killed the monk and the blind man and had the boy taken to a certain mountain from where he told his men to throw the boy down. However, all the king's men fell to their death and the boy returned alone to the king.

The king then sent him with another party of men, instructing them to take him by ship to the middle of the ocean and to throw him overboard. Again, all the king's men were drowned and the boy returned alone to the king.

The boy then told the king that he would be able to kill him only by shooting an arrow at him while saying, "In the name of the Rabb (Lord) of this boy." The king carried the order out. Seeing this, the people cried out, "We believe in the Rabb of this boy!"

The king was now worried because whereas he had killed one person, there were now thousands more. After discussing with important men of his kingdom, the king then instructed his soldiers to dig trenches and to fill the trenches with fire. Thereafter, he told them to throw in the fire all those who refused to give up their Imān. In this way, many people were burnt to death. Not long thereafter, Allāh ﷻ destroyed the king and all his men.

My Beloved Youngsters

Look at how one boy gave his soul over to the Creator of souls and became an invitation to Imān for so many others. One person sacrificed his life for the life of so many others. Do we even have the courage to speak about our Deen? What can we do for our Deen?

The least we can sacrifice is to make sure that we do not break even a single command of the Deen and also to make sure that we call people towards this Deen and towards carrying out every Sunnah of our beloved Prophet ﷺ.

The Cow and the Obedient Son

Among the youngsters of Isrāeel there lived a very rich man; he had a cousin who was poor and who was also his only inheritor. The latter felt that the former was slow to die and so he killed him in order to acquire his estate. He then carried him to another village and hid his body there. Pretending that he was seeking revenge, he took some people to Sayyidunā Moosā عليه السلام, accusing them of the murder. They proclaimed their innocence before Sayyidunā Moosā عليه السلام, who was not sure of what really happened. They asked him to pray to Allāh ﷻ to expose the true murderer. He ordered them to slaughter a cow, the story of which is related in the Holy Qur'ān, **"They said, Do you make fun of us?" (2:67)** Meaning, 'We ask you about the murderer, yet you order us to slaughter a cow!'

They said that because of the apparent difference between the two matters and because they did not know the wisdom behind his request. Sayyidunā Moosā عليه السلام said, **"I take Allāh's refuge from being among the ignorant or foolish ones." (2:67)** Meaning, 'I seek refuge in Allāh 🕮 from being among those who mock the believers'.

When the people realised that the command to slaughter a cow was really from Allāh 🕮, they asked Moosā 🕮 to describe it for them. Had they slaughtered any cow, that would have been enough for them; however, they were severe upon themselves and so Allāh 🕮 was severe in dealing with them. And there was wisdom behind that.

Prior to that time, there was a righteous man whose son was still a young boy. The father owned a young cow, which he took to a field and said, "O Allāh 🕮, I leave this with You for safekeeping until my son grows up." The man died and the cow remained in the field. At the time of the story, the cow was neither old nor young and it fled from all those who saw it or came near it. The son, now of age, was obedient to his mother. He would divide his nights into three parts; he would pray for one-third of the night, he would sleep for one-third and he would sit with his mother for one -third.

In the mornings, he would go to gather wood, which he would then carry on his back until he reached the marketplace, where he would sell the wood for whatever price Allāh 🕮 willed. He would then give one-third of the profits to charity, he would eat from the proceeds of one-third, and he would give one-third to his mother.

One day, his mother said to him, "Your father has left behind for you a young cow, and he asked Allāh 🕮 to keep it safe for you in such and such field, so go there and pray to the Lord of Ibrāheem, Ismā'eel, Ishāq and Ya'qoob ﷺ to return that cow to you. The sign that it is the right cow is that when you will look at it, you will imagine that the rays of the sun are coming out from its skin." It was called the golden one because of its yellowness and its beauty.

The young boy went to the field indicated to him. There he saw a cow grazing, and it was the very one that his mother described to him. He called out loudly, "I ask you to come by the Lord of Ibrā-heem, Ismā'eel, Ishāq and Ya'qoob ﷺ." It came to him in a hurry until it was standing in front of him; he took hold of its neck in order to lead it. By the Will of Allāh ﷺ, the cow spoke, saying, "O' young man who is obedient to his mother! Ride me, for that is eas-ier for you." The young boy said, "My mother did not order me to do that; rather she said, 'take it by its neck'."

The cow said, "Go, for indeed, if you ordered for a mountain to be cut from its roots so that it would go with you, it would have gone with you because of your obedience to your mother." The young boy then took the cow to his mother and she said to him, "Indeed you are poor, you have no wealth and gathering wood during the daytime is very difficult upon you and so is standing in the night. So go and sell this cow."

The young boy said, "And how much should I sell it for?" She said, "For three Dinārs, and do not sell it without first seeking counsel with me." The cow was as his mother said, worth three Dinārs; when the boy reached the marketplace, Allāh ﷺ sent to him an angel, in order to see his ability and in order to test him how obedient he was to his mother, though Allāh ﷻ had full knowledge of that.

The angel said to him, "For how much will you sell this cow?" He said, "For three Dinārs and I stipulate the pleasure of my mother (in this transaction)." The angel said, "I will pay six Dinārs, but you must not seek the counsel of your mother."

He said, "If you gave me money that weighed as much as this cow, I would not take it except with the pleasure of my mother." He then returned with the cow to his mother and told her of what had happened. She said, "Return and sell it for six Dinārs, but stipulate my pleasure."

He went to the marketplace and the angel came again and said, "You sought the command of your mother?" He said, "She ordered me not to sell it for less than six, on condition that I first seek her permission."

The angel said, "Then I will give you twelve, on the condition that you do not first seek her command." He refused, returned to his mother and informed her of what happened. She said, "Indeed the one who was coming to you is an angel in the shape of a man in order to test you." She instructed her son to ask him if he comes again. "Do you order us to sell this cow or not?" The young boy did in fact pose that question and the angel asked him to go to his mother and say to her, "Keep this cow! For indeed Moosā ﷺ, the son of Imrān, will buy it from you for the one who was murdered from the youngsters of Isrāeel. Do not sell it except for enough Dinārs that can fill its skin."

Allāh ﷻ decreed that the youngsters of Isrāeel had to slaughter that exact cow. As they continued to ask the description of the cow that they were supposed to slaughter, Moosā ﷺ described the cow that belonged to the obedient son, which was his reward for his obedience to his mother - a blessing, favour and mercy from Allāh ﷻ. When he stipulated the said price, which was of course very high, they had no choice but to buy it from him.

Allāh ﷻ ordered Moosā ﷺ to command his people to strike the corpse of the one who was murdered, and when they did that, he stood alive by the Will of Allāh ﷻ. And he said, "Such and such person killed me," referring to his cousin and then he died again in that very place. His murderer was thus prevented from inheriting his estate.

10 Rules to Start the Day

1. Today I will not strike back
If someone is rude, if someone is impatient, if someone is unkind, I will not respond in the same manner.

2. Today I will ask Allāh ﷻ to bless my "enemy"
If you come across someone today who treats you harshly or unfairly. I will quietly ask Allāh ﷻ to bless that individual. I understand the "enemy" could be a family member, neighbour, co-worker or a stranger.

3. Today I will be careful about what I say
I will carefully choose and guard my words being certain that I do not spread gossip.

4. Today I will go that extra mile
I will find ways to help share the burden of another person.

5. Today I will forgive
I will forgive any pain or injuries that come my way.

6. Today I will do something nice for somebody, but I will do it secretly
I will reach out secretly and bless the life of another.

7. Today I will treat others the way I wish to be treated
I will practice the golden rule, "do unto others as I would have

them do unto me," with everyone I encounter.

8. Today I will raise the spirits of someone I discouraged
My smile, my words, my expression of support can make the difference to someone who is wrestling with life.

9. Today I will nurse my body
I will eat less, I will eat only healthy foods. I will thank Allāh 🕮 for my body.

10. Today I will grow spiritually
I will spend a little more time in Salāh and Du'ā. I will begin reading something spiritual and inspirational. I will find a quiet place (at some point during the day) and contemplate on the purpose of life.

The Difference in Intention

There was a large tree in a village, wherefrom the inhabitants would benefit greatly. The bark of this tree had medicinal properties which the people would take to the city and sell. In this way they prospered and benefited. They had benefited so greatly from this tree, that some of them began worshipping it, thereby making the tree an object of worship.

As the years passed, a pious man came and settled in this village. When he saw that the people were worshipping this tree, he became angry.

When he saw them engaging in Shirk (polytheism), his eyes shed tears of blood. His anger became so uncontained, that he proceeded to his house to fetch an axe to chop the tree down. He was on his way, when Shaytān suddenly appeared before him in a human form.

Shaytān asked him, "Sir, where are you off to?"

The man replied, "The people are worshipping a tree and I am on my way to chop it down!"

Shaytān said, "You return and continue with your own work."

Upon hearing this, the man retorted, "Never, never! I will most certainly not return until I have accomplished what I have started out to do. If I return without having chopped the tree down, what answer will I give to Allāh ﷻ? I am going to chop down the tree so that the people stop committing Shirk."

Shaytān insisted, but the man did not relent. This resulted in a fight between the two of them which resulted in the man overwhelming Shaytān.

Shaytān then came up with another plan and said, "If you abandon your intention, then I will in return give you four gold coins daily. If you are keen on this trade then let me know."

Shaytān had made the effort on the man by offering him this gold.

The man thought for a while and said, "You must regularly bring me the gold coins otherwise I will certainly come and chop the tree down."

Shaytān replied, "Yes Sir, you will find these gold coins daily underneath your bed."

The pious man received his four gold coins for a few days, but then one day, he received nothing. He became very angry. He grabbed his axe and set off for chopping down the tree. On the way he again came across the Shaytān, who asked, "Sir! Where are you off to?"

The man replied, "I am going to chop down the tree, because you have ceased sending me the four gold coins daily."

Shaytān prevented him from going any further. They again became involved in a fight but this time Shaytān overpowered the man. The man was surprised and asked, "The last time I beat you, but this time you won, how is that?"

Shaytān smiled and replied, "Sir! The first time you set off to chop down the tree, you did so purely and solely for the pleasure of Allāh ﷻ. Your intention was pure.

However now your intention has changed. This time you have set out with intention of tricking me into resuming paying your four gold coins daily. This time, you should go back, lest I separate your neck from your body." Upon hearing this, the man returned full of shame.

My Beloved Youngsters!

When our intention is pure then we will be successful in every action, but if our intention is evil, then the same fate which befell this man will befall us as well.

Intention is the foundation of actions. The help and assistance of Allāh ﷻ will be in proportion to the sincerity of our intentions.

We should always endeavour to strive and make every action of ours purely for the pleasure of Allāh ﷻ.

Advice to My Beloved Youngsters

I want you to listen very carefully to the advices I wish to give you. Use them to correct your actions and do your best to practise on them all.

Please remember everything you will be told. Do you know how to remember them? Nothing can be stolen from the heart, so the only way something leaves the heart is when we use our eyes, ears and tongue in the wrong way. We must therefore make the intention that we will not use them wrongly. Now read on with attention:

1) When two elders are speaking or when an elder is talking to you, you should listen attentively and do not say anything in between unless they ask you something.

2) When your parents scold you for anything, immediately apologise and say that you will not do it again. It is bad to be stubborn and to prove that you were right.

3) If your parents scold you for something, just admit the wrong you did and never involve others just to shift the blame from yourself.

For example, if your father is scolding you for not getting something from the shop, don't say, "Mother told me to do something else," "Sister didn't iron my clothes, how could I go?" or "Brother took my cycle so I couldn't go."

4) Speak gently to all relatives and strangers, even when you are angry.

5) Never speak what is not necessary.

6) Never speak rudely.

7) When someone speaks angrily to you, explain nicely to them that there is no benefit in you both becoming angry. Tell the person that neither should he have ill feelings for you, nor should you have any for him and then make everything clear to him.

8) When your parents are angry remain silent. Wait until they are in a good mood before explaining why you think they should not have scolded you. Remember that you must do this with great respect.

Our elders tell us that we must speak so gently and respectfully to our parents like a servant speaks to an ill-tempered master. Let us think and see how many times every day do we speak rudely to them or backbite against them. Remember that the Holy Qur'ān states that you must not even say "uff!" to them.

This means that you must not tell them anything that will hurt their feelings. Infact, even if you take a deep sigh when they tell you something, it will also be regarded as saying "uff!". This was mentioned by Sayyidunā Ali ؓ. Therefore, saying anything that hurts them is Harām.

Holy Prophet ﷺ and the Old Lady

Once an old lady came to the Holy Prophet ﷺ and requested him to pray to Allāh ﷻ to favour her with Paradise. He said, "Old women will not enter Paradise."

Having said this, he left for Salāh and on hearing these words from the Holy Prophet ﷺ, the old lady began to weep.

When the Holy Prophet 🌸 returned after Salāh, Sayyidah Ā'ishah 🌸 told him that the old lady wept since she had heard that old women would not enter Paradise.

He told Sayyidah Ā'ishah 🌸 to tell her that old women would enter Paradise but having become youthful. The old lady upon hearing this smiled and became happy. (Tirmizi)

My Beloved Youngsters!

We all need to laugh and joke at times in order to relax and enjoy ourselves. Islām has allowed us to joke and laugh within limits, provided that we do not forget good behaviour and manners, nor lie.

Allāh 🌸 says in the Holy Qur'ān, **"O you who believe! Let not some people mock at other people; it may be that they are better than you." (49:11)**

A Muslim is forbidden to mock or laugh at other people. Only humour that is meant to please or cheer a person is permissible. Jokes that offend a person are not permissible.

1.   A joke that hurts the feeling of a person is not a joke but an insult.
2.   A joke that causes fear and worry is cruelty.
3.   A joke made up of lies and dishonesty is falsehood.
4.   Laughing at the weakness of a person is unkind and cruel.
5.   A joke is only acceptable if it makes a person happy and joyful.

6.   Too much laughter and joking hardens the heart and prevents a person from the remembrance of Allāh ﷻ.
7.   Joking and laughter is like salt in the food. Too much of it may spoil our Imān.
8.   Never make a joke of the commands of Allāh ﷻ and His beloved Prophet ﷺ.
9.   Never make jokes or fool around in the Masjid.
10.   The Holy Prophet's ﷺ laughter was no more than a smile.

You Ought to Know

What deeds can earn us the reward of Hajj?
There are certain deeds that will earn us the reward of Hajj. Allāh's ﷻ mercy is searching for people to shower itself upon. We must however remember that even after doing these deeds, Hajj will still be Fardh upon a person when he or she has the means to perform Hajj.

1) Performing Umrah during Ramadhān earns the reward of Hajj. The Holy Prophet ﷺ said that those who perform Hajj and Umrah are present in the court of Allāh ﷻ and when they make Du'ā to Allāh ﷻ, their Du'ā is accepted and when they ask for forgiveness, forgiveness is granted.

2) Looking at your parents with love earns the reward of Hajj.

Sayyidunā Abdullāh Ibn Abbās ؓ reports that the Holy Prophet ﷺ said, "When a person who treats his parents well and looks at them with affection, Allāh ﷻ writes for him the reward of an accepted Hajj for every glance he takes."

The Sahābah ؓ then asked, "Even if he looks at them one hundred times a day?" "Yes," replied the Holy Prophet ﷺ, "Allāh ﷻ is great and pure." None can stop Allāh ﷻ from giving as much reward as He wills.

3) The Ishrāq Salāh earns the reward of Hajj. Ishrāq Salāh is that Salāh which is performed approximately 10 minutes after sunrise. After the sun rises and becomes so bright that you cannot look at it, the time for the Ishrāq Salāh begins. The Salāh consists of at least 2 Rak'at. It is best (not compulsory) that a person remains seated in his place after performing the Fajr Salāh and continues making Dhikr or reciting the Holy Qur'ān until the sunrises. When the sun rises higher, he should then perform the Ishrāq Salāh.

Sayyidunā Anas Ibn Mālik ؓ reports that the Holy Prophet ﷺ said that when a person performs Fajr Salāh in Jamā'at, remains where he is and makes Dhikr and then performs 2 Rak'at Ishrāq Salāh after the sun rises, he will receive the reward of performing Hajj and Umrah.

4) Another Hadeeth tells us that when a person performs Wudhu at home and then leaves for the Masjid (to perform Salāh), he is like a person who enters into Ihrām and leaves for Hajj.

Respecting Elders

Junaid Baghdadi ﷺ used to be a famous wrestler. A man once came to the king of the time and asked, "I wish to fight your wrestler." "What!" the king exclaimed, "My wrestler is an extremely powerful man while you are a small and thin man. How can you ever fight him?" The man however refused to listen and insisted. The king eventually gave in and when the two fighters were about to wrestle with each other, the man whispered to Junaid Baghdadi ﷺ, "I am a Sayyid (relative of the Holy Prophet ﷺ) and I am very poor. You can do as you please."

As they fought, Junaid Baghdadi ﷺ suddenly fell down. There was a lot of shouting and noise from the people, but the king refused to accept it. He made the two men fight again, but again Junaid Baghdadi ﷺ was floored. When the same thing happened for the third time, the king gave the prize money to the little man.

The king then called for Junaid Baghdadi ﷺ and said, "Tell me the truth. What happened?" When Junaid Baghdadi ﷺ explained what had happened, the king was surprised to note that Junaid Baghdadi ﷺ could embarrass himself in front of so many people just because of his respect for a Sayyid. This was really a great act of bravery.

That night, Junaid Baghdadi ﷺ saw the Holy Prophet ﷺ in a dream. The Holy Prophet ﷺ said, "Congratulations, O Junaid! You were good to my relative because he was related to me. I shall also

75

do a good in return to you and have made Du'ā to Allāh ﷻ to make you respected throughout the world."

The following day, Junaid Baghdadi ﷺ left his occupation with the king and went out in search of Allāh's ﷻ pious saints. He eventually followed his uncle Saqtee ﷺ.

My Beloved Youngsters!

Remember that showing respect to elders increases a person's respect and does not reduce it. When someone respects his elders, people respect him and praise him even when he is not there. The Holy Prophet ﷺ commanded us in a Hadeeth that we should respect our elders and have mercy on youngsters.

We also learn that when Junaid Baghdadi ﷺ showed respect to a relative of the Holy Prophet ﷺ, Allāh ﷻ made the decision that respect will always be shown to him. Now if a person takes to his heart the actions of the Holy Prophet ﷺ and carries them out, how much respect will he not have in the sight of Allāh ﷻ?

It is therefore necessary for us to learn about the Sunnah practices and Du'ās of the Holy Prophet ﷺ from people with knowledge. By doing this, Allāh ﷻ will make the decision for us to be successful both in this world and in the Hereafter.

The Soldier and the City

One day whilst passing the wilderness, a saint came across a soldier who inquired, "Can you please point out to me the way to the city?" The saint pointed him in the direction of the graveyard. Disappointed by the wrong direction, the soldier came from the graveyard angrily and hit the saint on the head causing a serious wound. Thereafter he tied him with a rope and dragged him to the city. But when the people there told him that he had failed to recognise the great saint, the soldier argued, "But he told me the wrong way!"

The saint said, "My son, a town is a place where the population grows everyday, but here the population is decreasing and the number of graves are increasing. Is not the graveyard really a developing town?" The soldier recognised the saint and fell at his feet.

The Thief and the Gardener

A thief who believed in heavenly decision once broke into a garden and climbed a tree to pick some fruits. While he was eating the fruit on the branch of the tree, the owner of the garden suddenly appeared and shouted angrily, "Who are you? What are you doing here?"

"A subject of God is on a tree of God and with a hand made by God is picking and eating the fruit of God," answered the thief.

The gardener made him climb down the tree and tied him to a tree trunk. He then started to beat him with a thick stick. The thief, now in terrible pain, cried out, "Why are you beating me?"

"The stick of God in the hand made by God is striking a subject of God", the gardener answered.

My Beloved Youngsters!

We learn from this story that the thief could not get away by trying to steal the fruits from the garden. As Muslims we should not steal and we should not take something without asking the person who owns it.

A Parent's Love

Once, for some reason, a king gave orders for a father and his son to be punished.

"Tie them to those columns and give them each a hundred strokes with that cane. Start with the father, that would be much better."

The guard said to the father: "Stand still old man. Let me tie you. Now be ready for I'm starting, 1, 2, 3....98, 99, 100."

"All right, that's enough. Now it's the son's turn, tie him up and beat him," said the king.

"Come boy, stand beside this column and give me your hands," said the guard.

"Oh, no, please, for God's sake, don't beat my son. Stop beating!" the father pleaded.

"Huh! You endured a hundred strokes without saying so much a word. But now that your son is being beaten, how is it that you're wailing and weeping?" exclaimed the king.

"The first hundred strokes were not too hard to bear, but these strokes are tearing my heart apart. I can't stand the pain."

My Beloved Youngsters!

This story reminds us of how much our parents love us. We must also love our parents and respect them. The Holy Prophet 🕌 said, "Jannah (Paradise) lies beneath the feet of your mothers."

Three Arms Length for Everyone

Bahlool liked to visit the graveyards. "People here are good friends," he used to say, "They do not backbite."

Once, he sat in a corner of a graveyard. With a long stick he started prodding at some of the old skulls which were scattered around. Hārun Rashid, the king, passed by and saw him. "O Bahlool! What are you doing?"

"Oh, nothing very important," said Bahlool, "I am just trying to find out whether the skulls belong to kings or paupers. They are all the same."

"And what is the stick for?" Hārun asked. "Well, I am measuring the earth," replied Bahlool. "Measuring the earth? What are your findings?" Hārun joked.

"It is one and the same, O king," Bahlool retorted. "Three arm lengths for me, in spite of my poverty, and three arm lengths for you, in spite of your pomp and wealth."

Follow Your Heart

One beautiful morning, a farmer and his son were taking their donkey to the market to sell it. The father and his son were walking along together and the donkey was following them. They had not walked far when they passed a group of girls coming from the opposite direction.

"Just look at that," laughed one of the girls, pointing to the farmer. "What foolish people! They walk along the road when they could ride on their donkey!"

The old man quietly told his son to get on the donkey's back and they continued walking towards the market. Next they passed a group of men sitting by the side of the road, talking amongst themselves.

"See what I mean?" said one of the men, as the farmer and his son passed by. "The young have no respect for their old parents anymore. Get down you lazy boy, and let your father rest his legs!"

The son jumped down from the donkey's back and his father rode on the donkey. Soon they came across some women and youngsters.

"Look at the cruel man!" they exclaimed. "He is riding so fast that the poor boy can hardly keep up with him."

The farmer stopped and lifted the boy up behind him. They continued on their way and had almost reached the market when they met a shopkeeper on the road.

"Is that your own donkey?" asked the shopkeeper.

"Yes," replied the farmer.

"Then I am surprised at how you are treating him," said the shopkeeper.

"Two people on the back of one donkey is too many. He is sure to die from your strain. You should carry him instead!"

By this time, the farmer was getting used to taking other people's advice. He and his son got off the donkey and tied its legs together. Then they tied the rope to a long pole and carried the donkey upside down. But their donkey didn't want to be carried. By kicking and struggling, the donkey broke the rope holding its feet. It fell into a river near the road and was drowned. There was nothing the farmer could do except return home.

"Next time," said the farmer angrily, "I'll please myself."

An Intelligent Fish Seller

There was a king who was a generous and wonderful man. But his wife was stingy in nature.

Once the king went hunting along with the queen and on the way, they stopped by a big tree to rest in its shade. There, an Arab brought a fresh big fish to the king. The king was pleased and gave him 4,000 Dinārs for it.

The queen complained immediately, "This is wasting money. It goes far beyond generosity. You spent 4,000 Dinārs for a single fish! How much would you give away if you were given something more precious? If you paid less than that you'd be thought inconsiderate and if you wanted to pay more, the treasury would soon be emptied." She insisted that he had to get the money back from the Arab and pay him the real price of the fish. "How can I take back what I have already given him? That would not be kingly in manner," exclaimed the king.

"We can trick him and get the money back. For example, we can ask him if the fish is a male or a female. If he says male, we'll immediately say that we were looking for a female, and if he says female, we'll say we were looking for a male. This can be the best excuse to give him back the fish and have the money refunded."

"Oh, very well. You, Arab man, come over here and tell me if it was a male or a female fish." The clever Arab, who immediately understood the reasoning behind the question, replied, "It was neuter, Sir." The king liked his response and ordered that he be given another 4,000 Dinārs. The man was quite happy to receive another 4,000 Dinārs. When he turned around to leave, he dropped a coin. He bent down and picked it up.

The queen took advantage of this to say to the king, "Look how mean he is. He didn't leave a single coin for anybody else." The king said, "Hey you, come over here again. I gave you thousands of Dinārs but even so, when one of your coins dropped, you bent down and picked that single coin up. Don't you feel ashamed of yourself?"

The man gently replied, " Long live our king. I didn't do it because I'm a stingy person. It's just that the coin bears a picture of Your Majesty on it, and I thought it would be an insult to leave it on the ground to be stepped on by careless people." The king was so grateful that he granted him another 4,000 Dinārs.

The Great Famine

Once there was a great famine in Madeenah during the Khilāfah (rule) of Sayyidunā Abū Bakr 🕮. Muslims were much worried because all reserves of food and water had exhausted. Sayyidunā Abū Bakr 🕮 told everyone to pray to Allāh 🕮 for help and be patient.

Sayyidunā Uthmān 🕮 was returning with his caravan from Syria. There were a thousand camels carrying wheat, oil, raisin, foodstuffs and other merchandise. All the merchants from Madeenah gathered around him. They started putting up their offers to purchase the goods.

One of them said, "I will give you double the profit." Sayyidunā Uthmān 🕮 replied, "I have already been offered more." Another one said, "Ok no problem, I will give you four times the profit." Sayyidunā Uthmān 🕮 replied calmly, "I have been offered more than that."

The merchant said, "I will offer you five times the profit, because I know we can sell the goods at a very high price."

Sayyidunā Uthmān 🕮 smilingly said, "But I have already been offered more than that."

All the merchants got shocked. "Who could offer you more than this as all the merchants of Madeenah are here?" "Allāh 🕮 has

84

already promised me at least ten times the profit," replied Sayyidunā Uthmān ؓ and he smiled as he stood up.

"Be my witness, I give out all the camels with goods to the needy people for the pleasure of Allāh ﷻ," as Sayyidunā Uthmān ؓ raised his voice. All the worried and needy people received their share and prayed for Sayyidunā Uthmān ؓ.

Promises

Sayyidunā Huzaifah ؓ and his father Sayyidunā Yamān ؓ were on their way to Madeenah to meet with Rasūlullāh ﷺ when Abū Jahl got hold of them. When he asked them where they were going, they informed him that they intended to meet Rasūlullāh ﷺ in Madeenah.

"You are going there to fight against us," Abū Jahl shouted. When Sayyidunā Huzaifah ؓ assured him that all they intended doing was meeting Rasūlullāh ﷺ, Abū Jahl made them promise that they would not fight with the Muslims against him and the other polytheists. Sayyidunā Huzaifah ؓ was therefore forced to make the promise.

At the time, the Muslim army was already leaving for the Battle of Badr and Sayyidunā Huzaifah ؓ met them on the way. This was the great battle that Allāh ﷻ refers to as the day of Furqān (the day when the truth was separated from falsehood). It was the Muslims fighting in this battle who are referred to as the Badriyyeen, who have a very high rank among all the Sahābah 🕮 and about whom Rasūlullāh 🕮 stated that they were all forgiven by Allāh 🕮.

When Sayyidunā Huzaifah 🕮 met Rasūlullāh 🕮, he explained to Rasūlullāh 🕮 that they had been forced by Abū Jahl to promise not to fight in the battle. He had placed a sword to their necks and they had to make a promise to save their lives. Sayyidunā Huzaifah 🕮 therefore asked Rasūlullāh 🕮 to allow them to fight in the battle because their promise was one made under threat.

Rasūlullāh 🕮 however told them that since they had made a promise, they were forced to keep it. At that time, the Muslims needed every man they could get to fight for them because they were so few in number. They were only 313 in number with just seventy camels, two horses and eight swords. The other Sahābah 🕮 carried only sticks and rocks. However despite the need for more people, Rasūlullāh 🕮 still saw it more important for a person to keep his promise.

My Beloved Youngsters!

We learn from this incident that if a promise is made, it must be kept as far as it is possible. However there may be different situations at different times that will not be like this. It is therefore necessary to always ask the scholars whenever such occasions arise.

What Answer will I Give to Allāh ﷻ

Sayyidunā Umar ؓ was the second Caliph of Islām and ruled nearly half the world. Even the emperors of Rome and Persia shivered when they heard his name. His son Sayyidunā Abdullāh ؓ was once travelling somewhere when he became very hungry. When he saw a shepherd with some goats, he thought that he should ask him for some milk to stop the hunger.

"Could you please give me a glass of milk to drink so that my hunger could stop?" he asked the shepherd. "I don't mind giving you some, but the goats do not belong to me and I have no permission to give you any."

Now Sayyidunā Abdullāh ؓ was taught by his father, who saw to it that all Muslims of the Muslim Empire were practising on the Deen. He taught his son very well and also taught him wisdom. Sayyidunā Abdullāh ؓ decided to test the shepherd, so he said, "If you listen to something I have to say, you will benefit very greatly." "What is it?" the shepherd asked.

Sayyidunā Abdullāh ؓ then explained, "I shall buy one goat from you and give you the money, I shall then have milk to drink and when I wish, I can also slaughter it and have meat. You will then have some money for yourself and if your master asks where the one goat has gone, you may tell him that a wolf ate it."

87

As soon as he suggested this the shepherd asked, "Dear Man! Then where is Allāh 🕌? Where is Allāh 🕌?" Sayyidunā Abdullāh ﷺ was very happy to hear this and told the shepherd, "As long as there are people like you on Earth, there will always be good and success coming to the Ummah."

It is the concern for the Ākhirah (Hereafter) that makes a person alone in a forest realise that Allāh 🕌 is watching and that he will have to answer to Allāh 🕌 for all his actions. Even though some benefit is received in this world, the fact is that it will all be lost in the Ākhirah.

My Beloved Youngsters!

This story teaches us to be aware of Allāh 🕌 at all times and that we must never spoil our Ākhirah for a little benefit of this world. We must never use anybody's things without their permission.

To the Students of Deen

I always wanted to reach the top,
And to get there I know, I have to climb every rock.

I know this knowledge cannot be sold,
This road is bumpy as I was told.

I've got ups and downs, but this is my call,
Because success is about rising after we fall.

This is a legacy you just can't buy,
A light from Allāh ﷻ that does not die.

This is a message to the students of Deen,
Something awaits for us that hasn't been seen.

The mountain may be high and the rocks will be cold,
But on top something awaits, better than diamond and gold.

So carry on climbing with your dignity and pride,
Don't let anything confront you, or put you to a side.
All I say is watch your actions coz they just might make you fall,
It's not in our hands; it's up to Allāh ﷻ who He calls.

A Story of Allāh's ﷻ Greatness

My Beloved Youngsters!

Remember that when a person's heart is filled with love for Allāh ﷻ, Allāh ﷻ allows the person to do things that nations put together cannot achieve. In the seventh century after Hijrah, the Muslims became so negligent that the Tartars swept over them and captured their lands from them. In a single day, the Tartars killed a hundred and fifty thousand Muslims in Baghdad. In fact, the Muslims were so frightened of the Tartars that they used to say that if a person ever heard that the Tartars were defeated, they should never believe it.

Darband was a city that the Tartars once intended to attack. When the people of the city heard this, they left everything behind and ran away. It was only Shaykh Muhammad Darbandi ﷺ who remained in the Masjid with his servant. When the Tartar prince and his soldiers entered the town, they were stunned to see how cowardly their enemy was to leave so much wealth and luxuries behind and flee.

The prince sent his men to see whether anyone at all was in the city. When they discovered that there were two men in the Masjid, the prince instructed that the two be captured and brought to him. The two were therefore brought before the prince in chains.

Here are the words they exchanged:

Prince: Did you not know that we were coming to the city?
Shaykh: We certainly did.
Prince: Then why did you not run away?
Shaykh: We were sitting in Allāh's ﷻ house.
Prince: Do you not know that we have swords and that we can have you tied up in chains?
Shaykh: What can these chains do?
Prince: What do you mean?
Shaykh: These chains can do nothing to us.
Prince: What?!! None but ourselves can free you from those chains!!
Shaykh: No one can free us?

Shaykh Muhammad Darbandi ﵀ became angry and stood up saying, "Allāh ﷻ!" With the name of Allāh ﷻ, the chains snapped like old threads and the prince was terrified. He then told his men to free the Shaykh and to allow him to live in the city. The prince then started to like the Shaykh and used to visit him often. The prince eventually became a Muslim and because of this, other princes also became Muslims. In this manner, Allāh ﷻ made the empire a Muslim empire.

Lesson: We learn that when fear of Allāh ﷻ is in a person's heart, he knows well that nothing and no one else can benefit or harm him and therefore fears no one else. On the other hand, when a person does not fear Allāh ﷻ, he has no peace at all in this world.

My Beloved Youngsters!

We should also have this strong connection with Allāh ﷻ and our actions must show that we think of Allāh ﷻ. When a youngster listens to what his parents say and does not trouble his brothers and sisters at home, people know that he respects and loves his parents. Similarly, when we do things that please Allāh ﷻ like respect and obey our parents and teachers, then too people will know that we love and fear Allāh ﷻ.

The Old Sock

A wise and pious rich man, sensing his approaching death, called his son to his side and gave him these instructions: "My son, I shall be leaving you very shortly. On the day when I die, and they have washed my body and come to wrap it in the shroud, I want you to put one of my socks on my foot. This is my final request to you."

Soon after this, the old man did indeed die, leaving behind his goods and property, his youngsters and his dependents, family, friends, acquaintances and neighbours attended his funeral. The body had been washed and was almost completely wrapped in the shroud, when the son remembered his father's wish. Finding one of his old socks, he handed it to the washer of the dead, saying, "In accordance with my father's last request, please put this sock on his foot."

"That is quite impossible," said the man. "Such a thing is utterly prohibited in Islām. I cannot act against Islām." Despite this valid objection, the son insisted, "That was my father's final request; it must certainly be carried out."

The washer of the dead was unmoved. "If you won't take my word for it," he said. "Go and ask a Mufti. He will confirm what I tell you, that it is not permissible." Holding up the funeral, they consulted the preachers and scholars, all of whom declared that this was not permissible in Islām. Just then, an aged friend of the deceased interrupted the debate with these words to the son: "My boy, your late father entrusted me with a letter which I was to hand over to you after his departure. Here, this letter belongs to you." So saying this, he gave him an envelope. Taken by surprise, the boy opened the envelope and read out the contents of his father's letter.

"My son, all this wealth and property I have left for you. Now you see at the last moment, they won't even let you give me an old sock to wear. When you yourself come one day to be in my condition they will also refuse to let you keep anything but your shroud. Eight yards of shroud are all you will be able to carry over from this fleeting world into the Hereafter. So pull yourself together and be prepared. Spend the fortune I have left you, not for the satisfaction of desires, but in ways pleasing to Allāh ﷻ, that you may achieve honour in both worlds."

An Atheist Teacher Meets Her Match

One day a young girl was sitting down in the classroom. A teacher was going to explain the evolution theory to the youngsters. The teacher asked a little boy, "Harry, do you see the grass outside?" Harry said, "Yes." "Go outside and look at the sky," the teacher asked. He came back and said, "I saw the sky." The teacher slyly remarked, "Did you see God?" "No," he replied. "That's my point, you can't see God, he is not there!"

93

The little girl spoke up and wanted to ask the boy some questions. Little Zaynab spoke, "Harry do you see the grass outside?" "Yes," said Harry getting bored of the same question. "Do you see the teacher?" "Yes," he replied. The girl asked her last question, "Do you see her brain?" "No," he remarked. Zaynab spoke, "Then according to what we are taught in school, she must not have one!" "For we walk by faith, not by sight!"

Honesty Knows No Defeat

A man purchased a piece of land from another man. While digging the land the new owner found in it a pot full of gold. He said to the former owner, "Take this gold because it is yours. I had only purchased the land and not the gold which belongs to you."

"I have sold the land along with whatever it holds to you. I can't accept it as it now belongs to you," said the former land owner.

The two men brought their issue to another man whom they accepted as their judge. The judge, realising the delicacy of the matter, asked them if each of them had any youngsters. "Allāh ﷻ has blessed me with a son," said one of the two.

"I too have been blessed with a daughter," said the other. Hearing this the judge said, "Each of you should give his child in marriage to that of the other and spend the money on their wedding ceremony!"

From an Old Father

Dear Son/Daughter…
The day that you see me old, have patience and try to understand me. If I get dirty when eating, if I cannot dress, have patience. Remember the hours I spent teaching it to you.

If, when I speak to you, I repeat the same things a thousand and one times do not interrupt me. Listen to me. When you were small, I had to read to you a thousand and one times the same story until you got to sleep.

When I don't want to have a shower, neither shame me nor scold me. Remember when I had to chase you with a thousand excuses I invented, so that you would want to bath.

When you see my ignorance on new technologies, give me the necessary time and do not look at me with your mocking smile. I taught you how to do so many things; to eat well, to dress well and to confront life.

When at some moment I lose my memory or the thread of our conversation, let me have the necessary time to remember and if I cannot do it, do not become nervous as the most important thing is not my conversation but surely to be with you and to have you listening to me. If ever I do not want to eat, do not force me. I know well when I need to and when not. When my tired legs do not allow me to walk. Give me your hand, the same way I did when you made your first steps.

My Beloved Youngsters!

The Holy Prophet ﷺ said, "Every righteous child who casts a look of mercy and affection upon his parents shall be granted for every look of his, rewards equivalent to that of an accepted Hajj." Those around the Holy Prophet ﷺ questioned, "O Messenger of Allāh ﷻ, even if he were to look at them a hundred times a day?" The Holy Prophet ﷺ replied, "Indeed! Allāh ﷻ is the Greatest and Most Kind.

In the Holy Qur'ān, it says, **"Your Lord has decreed that you worship none but Him and that you be kind to parents. Whether one or both of them attain old age in your life, say not to them a word of contempt, nor repel them, but address them in terms of honour. And, out of kindness, lower to them the wing of humility, and say, 'My Lord! Bestow on them Your Mercy even as they cherished me in childhood'." (17:23-24)**

Sayyidunā Anas Ibn Mālik ؓ narrates that the Holy Prophet ﷺ said, "Whosoever wants comfort, sustenance and long life should do good to his blood relations and treat his parents well." (Ahmad)

Sayyidunā Abū Hurairah ؓ reports that the Holy Prophet ﷺ once said, "May his nose be smeared in dust!" Someone asked to whom he was referring to, the Holy Prophet ﷺ said, "The man, who has aged parents and did not take the opportunity to secure Paradise."

(Bukhāri, Muslim)

The Clever Businessman

A king once had the announcement made that whoever speaks a lie in his kingdom will have to face the righteous judge and will then receive a very severe punishment. After hearing this announcement, the people started to stay away from each other, fearing that someone may accuse them of lying.

The king and his minister disguised themselves one day and went out into the city. When they met a businessman, the following conversation took place:

King: How old are you?

Businessman: Twenty years old.

King: How much money do you have?

Businessman: Seventy thousand.

King: How many youngsters do you have?

Businessman: One.

The king and the minister then returned to check their register. They however found out that the man had lied to them. They therefore called for him and the following conversation took place this time:

King: You said that you were twenty years old, which was a lie. Your punishment will therefore be…

Businessman: You must first prove that I was wrong.

King: Our register here says that you are now sixty-five years old.

Businessman: Dear Sir! It was only twenty years of my life that I spent in peace and happiness. I therefore regard only those years as my life.

King: When we asked you about your money, you said that you only had seventy thousand whereas the register shows that your money cannot even be counted.

Businessman: Although I have so much wealth, it was seventy thousand that I spent to build a Masjid and because that will be of use to me in the Ākhirah, I regard only that to be my true wealth.

King: But when we asked about your youngsters, you said that you have only one, whereas you have five.

Businessman: Four of my youngsters are worthless because they have terrible character and are evil people. However, one is a good child whose character is excellent. It is only him that I regard as my child because only he can be of use in the Hereafter.

The king was very pleased with the answers and said, "It is truly only the years of peace and happiness that can be regarded as life and only that wealth is really wealth, which was spent for Allāh ﷻ and which will benefit one in the Hereafter. As for youngsters, it is only the ones with good character and who do good deeds who can be called ones' youngsters.

My Beloved Youngsters!

The answers that the businessman gave are really what our Deen says. Only that part of a person's life can really be called life, which is spent in the remembrance of Allāh ﷻ. Similarly, only that wealth can be called wealth, which is spent to please Allāh ﷻ and the youngsters are a form of Sadaqah for their parents after their deaths.

Allāh ﷻ told Sayyidunā Nooh عليه السلام about his son who did not accept Imān, "He is really not from your family." We must also spend all we have for the pleasure of Allāh ﷻ because the Holy Prophet ﷺ said, "The intelligent person is he who prepares for his death." We must therefore keep on the straight path and tell others to do the same.

My Mother's Love

One evening, I came up to my mother in the kitchen while she was preparing dinner and handed her a piece of paper that I had been writing on. After my mother dried her hands on an apron, she read it and this is what it said:

For cutting the grass: £5.00
For cleaning up my room this week: £1.00
For going to the store for you: 50p
Baby-sitting my baby brother while
you went shopping: 25p
Taking out the garbage: £1.00
For getting a good report card: £5.00
For cleaning up the yard: £2.00

Total owed: £14.75

Well, my mother looked at me standing there and I could see the memories flashing through her mind. She picked up the pen, turned over the paper I had written on and this is what she wrote:
"For the nine months I carried you while you were growing inside me: No Charge

For all the nights that I've sat up with you, cared and prayed for you: No Charge

For all the trying times and all the tears that you've caused through the years: No Charge

For all the nights that were filled with dread and the worries I knew were ahead: No Charge

For the toys, food, clothes and even wiping your nose: No Charge

My dear son, when you add it all up, the cost of my love is: No Charge..."

When I finished reading what my mother had written, tears started rolling from my eyes and I looked straight at my mother and said, "O mother, I love you so much."

And then I took the pen and in great big letters I wrote: "PAID IN FULL".

My Beloved Youngsters!

We will never know how much our parents are worth till we become a parent ourselves. Be a giver not an asker, especially with your parents there is a lot to give, besides money.

Advice: If your mother is alive and close to you, give her a big kiss and hug and ask her for forgiveness. If she is far away, call her, if she passed away, pray for her.

The Jealous King

Imām Sha`bi ﷺ, a distinguished scholar from the early generations of Islām, related the following incident:

Abdul Mālik Ibn Marwān once sent me to the king of Rome. When I reached him, he asked me a number of questions, and I answered each one of them. In general, ministers would not stay with him for a long time; however, in my case, he detained me for a number of days, until I myself requested permission to leave.

When I was determined to leave he said to me, "Are you of the household of your king?" I said, "No, I am simply a common man among the Muslims." He whispered something to one of his guards, and then a card was given to me. He said, "When you hand over the letters you have with you to your king, give him this card as well."

When I returned home, I handed over many letters to Abdul Malik but I forgot to give him the card. Only at a later time did I remember, and I hastened to give it to him. After reading it, he said to me, "Did he say anything to you before giving you this card?" I said, "Yes, he asked me, "Are you of the household of your king?" I told him no, but rather that I am simply a common man from among the Muslims."

I was parting from the caliph, but when I reached the gates, I was called back to him. When I was again standing in front of him, he said, "Do you know what is on this card?" I said, "No." He said, "Read it."

On it was written: I am amazed at the people who have among them such a man, yet they have chosen another king!

I said to him, "By Allāh ﷻ, If I had known what was written on it, I would not have carried it with me! He only said this because he has not seen you."

Abdul-Malik said, "Do you know why he really wrote it?" I said, "No." He said, "He was jealous of me having you, so he tried to change my heart against you, hoping that I would kill you and so that the Muslims would not benefit from your knowledge."

The news of what happened reached the king of Rome, who said, "He was right in knowing my intention."

Childhood of Some Elders

Every child grows up into an adult, but the childhood of every person is different. Every person who grew up to be a saint, a great person or a scholar had some special incidents in their childhood days.

We must take lessons from these incidents and remember that to be successful in this world and the Hereafter, we must try and follow their examples.

Shaykh Sa'di ﷺ says, "When I was a little boy, I went with my father to the Eid festival. However, I left his side and got lost. I then started to cry and when my father found me, he twisted my ear and scolded me for leaving his side. This incident stuck in my mind to this day and guided me throughout my life. I learnt from this that the person who leaves the side of pious people will get lost in the festival of this world."

My Beloved Youngsters!

When a child is born, he is the light in his parents' eyes. However, because he is grown up in the lap of his mother, it can happen that the youngsters are spoilt by their mothers and then become stubborn and cry for every little thing. The stories of the pious people teach us that when youngsters are not stubborn and do not cry for every little thing, they benefit greatly afterwards.

It may have happened some years ago that when your mother gave all of you milk to drink, you were stubborn and you wanted it all to yourself. Your elder brother then drank his share and yours as well. Although this will end here for us, Shaykh Rasheed Ahmad Gangohi ﷺ said that such an incident taught him that being stubborn will cause you to lose even what is yours. He therefore never behaved stubbornly throughout his life.

We must also make an attempt to get rid of all the bad habits we have in ourselves and when someone tells us about a bad habit in us, we must never argue about it, but rather listen and make an

Shaytān Vomits

Sayyidunā Umayyah Ibn Makhshi ⚔ says that a man was busy eating when the Holy Prophet ﷺ came there. The man had started to eat without reciting Bismillāhir Rahmānir Raheem. He had almost finished eating and had only one last morsel left in his plate when he remembered that before eating he had forgotten to recite:

$$ بِسْمِ اللهِ الرَّحْمٰنِ الرَّحِيْم $$

Bismillāhir Rahmānir Raheem

He remembered also that the Holy Prophet ﷺ taught them that when a person forgets to recite Bismillāh before eating and then remembers while he is still busy eating, he should recite:

$$ بِسْمِ اللهِ اَوَّلَهُ وَ اٰخِرَهُ $$

Bismillāhi awwalahu wa Ākhirahu

He then recited the Du'ā. When he recited it, the Holy Prophet ﷺ looked at him and started to smile. The Holy Prophet ﷺ then said, "Shaytān was eating with him all the time but when he took Allāh's ﷻ name and recited, Bismillāhi awwalahu wa ākihirahu,

105

Shaytān vomited out everything that he had eaten. All that he ate came to an end with that small sentence."

My Beloved Youngsters!

The Holy Prophet 🌸 smiled when he saw all of this happen before his very own eyes. The Holy Prophet 🌸 taught us that when a person forgets to recite Bismillāh before eating and then remembers whilst he is still busy eating, he should recite, Bismillāhi Awwalahu wa ākihirahu. By doing this, Shaytān no longer has any share in the food and the blessings come back.

Fashion Confusion

As I walked in the street today,
I saw what seemed like a boy moving with the music beat.
I walked closer and then to my astonishment,
I saw it was not a boy but a girl.
Men grow their hair,
women want to get more fair.
everyone wants to be cool,
Not realizing that they look like nothing but fools.

Old women wear clothes to fit their kids,
men wear clothes designed for women,
the world now is in a fashion confusion.
A woman may seem dressed,

yet in the eyes of Allāh ﷻ she is not,
new fashion identity, where less has become more,
and the daily laws of Allāh ﷻ we ignore.
The degeneration of the Ummah, wouldn't you agree,
lies in the quest for a fashionable identity.

A Sign of Qiyāmah is Gender and Fashion confusion.

My Neighbours

Allāh ﷻ says in the Holy Qur'ān, **"Show kindness to your parents, your relatives, orphans, the needy and the neighbour." (4:36)**

Our neighbours, Muslims and non-Muslims need to be treated with special care and respect. They have rights over us just as our parents and relatives have rights over us.

The Holy Prophet ﷺ said, "He is not a true believer who eats to his fill while his neighbour remains hungry by his side."

Some neighbours have greater rights than others.
Neighbours are of Three Kinds:

1. A non-Muslim: He enjoys the rights of a neighbour.
2. A Muslim: He enjoys the rights of being a Muslim and a neighbour.
3. A relative: He enjoys 3 rights, a Muslim, a relative and a neighbour.

107

Rights of a Neighbour:

1. Visit him when he is sick.
2. Attend his funeral.
3. If he asks for a loan, give it if you can.
4. Feed him if he is hungry.
5. Give him clothes if he has no clothes.
6. Congratulate him on happy occasions.
7. Comfort him in times of difficulty and hardship.
8. Do not spread the faults of your neighbour.
9. Do not disturb the peace of your neighbour.
10. Do not harm your neighbour in anyway.

Our beloved Prophet ﷺ said, "Exchange gifts with each other, you will love each other." (Baihaqi)

Giving gifts shows our love and concern for others. It also creates our love and concern in the hearts of those who receive them. The exchange of gifts is, in fact an exchange of our good feelings for each other. It increases love and respect for each other.

Other titles from JKN Publications  JKN
PUBLICATIONS

Your Questions Answered

An outstanding book written by Shaykh Mufti Saiful Islām. A very comprehensive yet simple Fatāwa book and a source of guidance that reaches out to a wider audience i.e. the English speaking Muslims. The reader will benefit from the various answers to questions based on the Laws of Islām relating to the beliefs of Islām, knowledge, Sunnah, pillars of Islām, marriage, divorce and contemporary issues.

UK RRP: £7.50

Hadeeth for Beginners

A concise Hadeeth book with various Ahādeeth that relate to basic Ibādāh and moral etiquettes in Islām accessible to a wider readership. Each Hadeeth has been presented with the Arabic text, its translation and commentary to enlighten the reader, its meaning and application in day-to-day life.

UK RRP: £3.00

Du'ā for Beginners

This book contains basic Du'ās which every Muslim should recite on a daily basis. Highly recommended to young children and adults studying at Islāmic schools and Madrasahs so that one may cherish the beautiful treasure of supplications of our beloved Prophet ﷺ in one's daily life, which will ultimately bring peace and happiness in both worlds, Inshā-Allāh.

UK RRP: £2.00

How well do you know Islām?

An exciting educational book which contains 300 multiple questions and answers to help you increase your knowledge on Islām! Ideal for the whole family, especially children and adult students to learn new knowledge in an enjoyable way and cherish the treasures of knowledge that you will acquire from this book. A very beneficial tool for an educational syllabus.

UK RRP: £3.00

Treasures of the Holy Qur'an

This book entitled "Treasures of the Holy Qur'ān" has been compiled to create a stronger bond between the Holy Qur'ān and the readers. It mentions the different virtues of Sūrahs and verses from the Holy Qur'ān with the hope that the readers will increase their zeal and enthusiasm to recite and inculcate the teachings of the Holy Qur'ān into their daily lives.

UK RRP: £3.00